# BASEBALL STORIES FOR THE SOUL

## 50 STORIES, POEMS & OTHER SOULFUL INSPIRATIONS ABOUT AMERICA'S FAVORITE PASTIME

### W.C. MADDEN

Madden Publishing Co., Inc.
10872 Washington Bay Dr.
Fishers, IN 46038
wmadden@peoplepc.com

**Library of Congress Card Number: 00-192596**

Baseball stories for the soul: 50 stories, poems and other soulful inspirations about America's favorite pastime, compiled by W.C. Madden.

ISBN 0-9645819-2-2 (paperback)

Publisher:
Madden Publishing Co., Inc.
10872 Washington Bay Drive
Fishers, IN 46038

# Table of Contents

# Introduction

I had some ideas for poems and short stories while I was writing a book about baseball's first-year player draft for McFarland Publishing. However, I didn't have any avenue in which to deliver those stories to readers. So, I decided the best way was to prepare a book of poems and short stories from many different authors.

I advertised in the baseball newspapers and the Society for American Baseball Research for material that touched the heart. The response wasn't as great as I had hoped, but some writers were enthusiastic and submitted some good material. I also researched some information in the public domain to provide more material that readers may not have seen in awhile. The sports collection at the Joyce Sports Research Center at Notre Dame Library was one of the places in which I found a good collection of books published prior to 1925. Curator George Rugg helped me research some of the public domain material for this book.

The photos used in this book are in the public

domain and distributed by Desperate Enterprises, Inc. Contact them at 1-800-732-4859 or www.desperate.com for more information.

The stories and poems in this book will hopefully touch your soul like they did mine.

**Three-Finger Brown**

# Against all odds

**by W.C. Madden**

The road to the majors leagues is a long and winding for many and cluttered with casualties. For someone with a physical handicap, the road is well-nigh impossible. But a few players in the history of the game have overcome their physical handicap and made it to the top against all odds.

Many young boys are intrigued by trains. They love to watch them, play with models or ride in them. **Peter J. Wyshner** was no different. He would watch the steel giants chug by his home in Naticoke, Pennsylvania.

The six-year-old Lithuanian lad decided one day that he'd go for a ride on one of the trains. He chose a slow moving freight train as his target. When he grabbed for the ladder, he fell and his right arm was run over by the train. Doctors couldn't save the arm and had to amputate it.

The naturally right-handed boy would have to learn everything with his left hand. Peter took up an interest in baseball, but he knew it wasn't going to be an easy task to play. He first began as a batboy. Then he finally got his opportunity to play. A shoemaker helped him by making him a glove that allowed him to handle the ball quicker with his only arm. After he fielded a ball, he'd flip it up in the air while sticking the glove between his stump and his chest. Then he'd catch the ball coming down and throw it with his left arm, sort of like watching a juggler. He practiced harder and harder and got better and better.

Then at age 15, he saw a World Series game at Wrigley Field and that inspired him to become a professional. He knew he couldn't be like the Babe he watched play, but he could do other things better, like bunting and running. Pete began his professional career by playing semipro for his hometown. He changed his last name to Gray to make it easier for everyone to write or pronounce.

Gray ventured to Brooklyn, New York to tryout with the Buskwicks. After challenging the manager with a $10 bet, he made the team and played for two years there.

The war broke out in December 1941 and many professional players either drafted or volunteered to serve their country. Gray, of course, was 4F. He moved to Trois Rivieres, Quebec, which had a team in the Class C Canadian-American League. He spoke with the manager of the team by phone and was given a professional contract. The manager knew nothing of the missing arm and you can imagine the look on his face when he met Gray for the first time. But the outfielder surprised the manager and showed him he was well worth the contract.

In 1943, Gray went to the Southern Association to play. In his second year there, he stole 63 bases to tie a league record. Plus, he hit an astonishing .333. His accomplishments led the league to name him most valuable player.

In the off-season, the world champion St. Louis

Browns bought his contract from the Memphis Chicks for $20,000. Gray hit well in spring training and the Browns rewarded him with a start on Opening Day. He had made it to the majors!

However, the Browns used him sparingly during the season and he hit only .218 in 234 times at bat. St. Louis seemed more interested in using him as a drawing card. A couple of players actually thought he cost them the pennant that season.

The following season many of the wartime players were back for good, so Gray would not be needed. His notoriety had worn off as well. He went back to the minors. However, his dreams had been fulfilled. He had beaten all the odds of ever making it to the majors.

During the war, there was another player who was in a similar position as Gray. His name was **Bert Sheperd**. The left-handed hurler had struck out with three minor league teams before the war began then he was drafted in May 1942. He signed up for pilot training and learned to fly the P-38 Thunderbolt. After training, he was assigned to the 55th Fighter Group in England.

On May 21, 1944, Lieutenant Shepard was given a mission to attack an airdrome. Afterwards, he was looking forward to pitching in the first baseball game of the season for the squadron team, which he managed. As he was strafing the target, shells ripped through the plane and took off his left foot. Shepard tried in vain to control his craft. He crashed.

The lieutenant awoke a few days later in a German Hospital only to find out the doctors had removed his leg just below the knee. And he had a nasty head injury. Shepard was glad to be alive. He thought his baseball days were over. As he recovered, some fellow prisoners fashioned an artificial leg for him. He began to recover and found out he could still play baseball.

In February 1945, he was part of a prisoner exchange and he returned to the States. He went to Walter Reed Hospital to get fitted for a new artificial leg. While he was waiting for the prostetius, he was summoned to the Secretary of War's office. Secretary Robert Patterson asked him what he wanted. Shepard responded that he wanted to pitch in the major leagues. Patterson made a call to Clark Griffith, owner of the Washington Senators, and asked him to give Shepard a tryout. Griffith agreed.

Shepard reported to spring training much to the surprise of some players on the team. A few days later, newsreel crews came in and the Senators benefited from all the publicity. Griffith signed him as a pitching coach at first and allowed him to throw batting practice. He later appeared in some exhibition games.

Finally on August 4, 1945, Shepard was called on to pitch in a real game. Boston had just scored 12 runs and was making a rout of the game, so Shepard was called on to finish the game. The lefty with the limp showed the fans he could pitch by striking out the first batter to end the inning. He received a standing ovation. Sheperd pitched the remainder of the game and allowed only one run on three hits over five innings.

The Senators were fighting for the pennant that season, so Shepard was never used again. However, he was invited back the next season, but with all the players returning from the war, his chances of pitching again in the majors faded. He did play in the minors for several seasons to come.

Another player who overcame injuries to achieve success in the majors was **Mordecai Peter Centennial Brown**. At age seven, he accidentally put his right hand into his uncle's corn grinder. As a result his index finger had to be amputated just below the knuckle. To make matters worse, a few weeks later he broke the third and fourth fingers on the same hand. The fingers were bent and twisted, which added to his disformity.

Despite the knarled hand, he took up playing baseball for a local semipro team near his hometown of Nyesville, Indiana. He played third until one day the star pitcher got hurt and he volunteered to pitch. He discovered he had a natural curveball, because of the unique grip he had to put on the ball.

Former major leaguer player Ace Stewart knew Brown and urged him to play for Terre Haute in 1902. That led Miner–a nickname he picked up because he was coal miner before baseball–to the Western League and fame as he won 27 games for Omaha. "I think he will develop into a star of the first magnitude," a teammate of his commented The league leading recognition led the St. Louis Cardinals to purchase his contract. His major league career began slowly with a 9-13 record, but the Cardinals ended last that season and didn't provide him much run support.

Chicago Cubs manager Frank Selee was so impressed with Brown, he traded his star pitcher for him. It turned out to be a great trade for the Cubs. "Three Finger" helped the Cubs to pennants in 1906, 1907, 1908 and 1910. He was untouchable in the 1907 and 1908 World Series, compiling a 3-0 record and 0.00 ERA! In 1909 he led the league in wins (27), saves (7), complete games (32) games pitched (50) and innings pitched (343). He still holds the all-time National League record for lowest ERA in a season–1.04 in 1906. He was enshrined into the Hall of Fame in 1949. "All I know is that I had all the fingers I needed," Brown once said.

Before Brown, there was a player who had only one hand–**Hugh Daily**. As a boy, he was playing around in a Baltimore Theater when an English flintlock went off and bady injured his left hand. It had to be amputated.

To play baseball, he put a leather pad at the end of

the left arm to block the ball. He also learned to hit with one hand, but that skill wasn't as important, because he was a pitcher. The 25-year-old hurler debuted for the Buffalo Bisons in 1882 with a 15-14 record. The following year he went to Cleveland and improved to 23-19.

Daily jumped to the Union Association where he led the league in strikeouts. He tied a record with 19 K's in one game—a one-hitter. Three days later, he hurled another one-hit gem to become the first pitcher to throw back-to-back one hitters. When the association folded after a single season, Daily returned to the National League. However, his career was all downhill after that as he lost 26 of 33 games he started over the next three years. He left baseball and was never heard from again.

Another one-handed player was **Jim Abbott**, but his is a different story. The modern-day player was born without a right hand. Abbott dreamed about pitching in the majors when he was in Little League and he wasn't going to let that stop him. Working with his father, he developed a way to field and throw runners out with one hand. He practiced it until he perfected it.

Abbott was a natural pitcher and blew fastballs past hitters right from the start. As he grew older, he developed more pitches to his arsenal and he earned a scholarship to the University of Michigan.

The national media took an interest in the one-handed hurler and soon everyone knew of his talents. It made him nervous at first, but he became accustomed to cameras following him around. Then he was named to the US National Team. He led Team USA to victory in the Pan Am Games. His performance led to him being given the Sullivan Award, which had never been giving to a baseball player in the 58 years of existence. Then it was off to the Olympics, where he pitched the team to a gold medal.

After his senior year at Michigan, he was drafted in

the first round by the Anaheim Angels, who decided that Abbott was good enough to play in the majors. The Angels were right.

Abbot experienced a roller coaster career in the majors. His high point was a no-hitter for the New York Yankees in 1993. His low point was a 2-18 record with the Angels in 1996. In all, he pitched 10 seasons in the majors that ended with an 87-108 record. Upon retirement, Abbot said he was fulfilled by his career in the majors. "You have to have a positive attitude or you won't get anywhere," he said.

These players proved to themselves that they were up to the task at hand. They overcame their handicaps to achieve the measure of success they were after.

# The pinch-hitter

**by Eric Soderholm**

It was a warm day in August when history was made,
The people in the box seats were hunting for shade,
The bases were loaded and it was the last inning,
From the sound of the crowd, you knew we weren't win-
ning.

Then out of the dugout came Rickie Zisk,
And everybody knew that the bases would be kissed,
Legend tells of Casey at the Bat,
But today it was the Polack who tipped his hat.

The cursing and swearing came from the stands,
When Richie was waved back by Bob Lemon's hand,
An astonished look came over Zisk's face,
When Lemon said, "Solderholm's taking your place."

As Eric stepped from the dugout came a scream from a fan,

You can't hit Solderholm, the big Polack's our man.
Never before in history had they pinch-hit for Zisk,
Especially with a bad-knee free agent who was such a big
risk.

This has to be a mockery and a dirty, rotten shame,
To pinch-hit for a man who's a sure Hall of Fame,
Eric heard not a word as he strode to the plate,
He only noticed the crowd's eyes–they were full of hate.

God help me this one time, kept going through my mind,
If I ever get a hit, please make it this time,
Ryan looking in and thought, "This should be a cinch."
To throw three strikes by this rider of the bench.

Strike one was the call from the man in blue,
And four pitches later, it was three and two.
Now everything rode on the very next pitch,
Would Eric stay a poor man, or suddenly be rich.

Then the crack of the bat and a long drive to right,
And the back of Rudi's uniform was the only thing in sight,
Then from the roar of the crowd, there was a deafening
scream,
...Ah, then Eric fell out of bed. It was only a dream.

*(Soderholm wrote this poem on July 24, 1977, after hitting
two homers that helped the Chicago White Sox defeat the
Boston Red Sox. He played nine seasons in the majors with
the Twins, Sox, Rangers and Yankees.)*

# Gooden finds the Lord, himself

**by Bob Bellone**

Dwight Gooden remembers a moment from his early childhood when he was timid with a baseball clutched in his hand.

It may have been the last time.

With a gentle nudge from his father Dan, Dwight bashfully approached Al Kaline to get the Hall of Fame outfielder to sign the ball he had fouled off that spring day in Lakeland, Florida.

Seemingly overnight, Gooden himself was leaving people in awe as he pitched his way to stardom from Tampa's Belmont Heights Little League to Hillsborough High School to the big leagues.

On June 7, 1982, he was in the sports department of *The Tampa Tribune* to await his destiny in the Major League Baseball amateur draft. The visit was short for Gooden, who was selected fifth overall by the New York Mets.

In 1983, he set a Carolina League record with 300 strikeouts and was named Minor League Player of the Year by *Baseball America.*

Gooden got the call to the majors a year later. Among his achievements by season's end, he was selected by the Baseball Writers Association of America to become the youngest National League Rookie of the Year in history; became the first newcomer to lead the majors in strikeouts with 276, averaging a record of 11.4 per nine innings; set a National League standard by fanning 32 batters in consecutive September starts, which also tied the major-league mark at the time; and, pitched a one-hitter in a 10-0 victory over the Chicago Cubs.

All the while, Mets fans urged on Gooden by keeping count of his strikeout victims with the "K" placards they would hang in the right-field corner of Shea Stadium. Suddenly, the 19-year-old flamethrower was holding New York City in the palm of his right hand.

"I think my first year, I didn't notice it a whole lot," he said of his widespread fame. "It's kind of like you're successful, but you're doing something you really enjoy doing."

Dwight was only beginning to make life miserable for batters. He began the 1985 season as the youngest pitcher ever to start an Opening Day game. He finished with a 24-4 record and a 1.53 ERA to become the most youthful Cy Young Award recipient. By then he had taken a shine to center stage. "I loved it," he explained. "You kind of felt like a singer or an entertainer because that day you felt it was your show."

Accordingly, he fed off the cheering crowds. "I remember times taking a peek up there at the K Corner to see how many Ks I had, because I wanted at least 10 every game. Things like that was a tremendous feeling."

Gooden eventually got his highs through the misuse

of drugs and alcohol. His third related suspension from baseball cost him the entire 1995 season. And nearly his life.

Only a day after then-acting commissioner Bud Selig handed down the ban in September 1994, the pitcher was on the brink of suicide. "I was right there," said Gooden, who had put a gun to his head as he dwelled upon the punishment and his inability to stay clean. "I was sick and tired of myself, because not only do you destroy yourself, but you destroy your family or anyone that cares anything about you."

Gooden told the *New York Daily News* two years after the episode that he hadn't made up his mind to pull the trigger when his wife Monica entered the bedroom. Screaming hysterically, she grabbed the gun and ran.

"He was like the best pitcher on the planet," remembered former Texas Rangers left-hander Kenny Rogers, a teammate of Gooden upon his return to baseball with the New York Yankees in 1996. "He got so much, so quick–the exposure and the money, all you can handle. And then to be thrown into New York. There's more things to get into, good and bad."

Dwight found his share of both in the Tampa Bay area during his year out of the game. He would regularly attend church with his mother Ella Mae, but he continued to hang out with the wrong crowd. "I was kind of on the fence," he said.

Two years ago he came down on the side of Christianity. "My thinking was, 'I've tried drinking. I've tried drugs. Why not try that? Why not turn my life over?'"

Beforehand, Gooden had a different set of priorities.

"Baseball was No. 1. My wife and my family were secondary," he explained. "Now, I put the Lord first, then my family, then baseball."

It shows.

"He's one of the nicest guys you'll ever be around," said Devil Rays pitcher and former Yankees teammate Dave Eiland. "That's what struck me the most about him when I first met him. When I walked into the clubhouse in New York, he was the first one to come up to me and introduce himself. You remember those types of things."

Rays first baseman Fred McGriff recalls a lot of things about Gooden, having grown alongside him in Tampa baseball circles. "He was awesome in high school and in Little League," said McGriff, a Jefferson High product. "He was striking out 15 or 16 guys. When he went up to the big leagues, he did the same thing."

Gooden seemed to be on a fast track to Cooperstown before his career derailed. But with his 200th victory in sight, the 35-year-old hasn't given up hope. "It would definitely be an honor," he said. "Especially after the things I went through off the field."

On the mound, few were better than the pitcher who was named to four National League All-Star teams in his first five years and led the Mets to the 1986 World Series title.

Gooden also won 14 games for the World Champion Yankees in 1996. Among them was a no-hitter over the Seattle Mariners in the Bronx, inspired by his father listening on radio from a Tampa hospital bed only hours before undergoing double-bypass heart surgery. "The first couple of innings I was kind of drifting a little bit, thinking about him," Gooden said. "In about the sixth inning, this peace came over me and I got totally focused and pitched. I just knew the Lord was working through me."

Within hours after the game, the renewed baseball hero was on a plane bound for Florida. "I didn't get much sleep that night," said Gooden, who delivered the game ball the next day to his father at the hospital.

"He's a Hall of Fame pitcher," McGriff said. "I

can't believe there are too many guys in the history of the game that have pitched better than Dwight."

*(Editor's Note: Shortly after Bob wrote this story, the Tampa Bay Devil Rays cut Gooden from their roster. He sat at home for nearly a month until he got a call from the Yankees. He pitched at Triple-A for a few games before being called to pitch against his original team—the Mets. Gooden started the game, threw five innings and left with the score tied 2-2. The Yankees rallied for a run in the sixth and went on to win to give Dwight the win. He was the happiest player on the field.)*

*(Reprinted with permission from SportsTime Magazine, Tampa, Florida. Bellone is a freelance sports writer in Tampa, Florida.)*

# Casey at the bat

**by Ernest L. Thayer**

It looked extremely rocky for the Mudville nine that day,
The score stood four to six with but an inning left to play.
And so, when Cooney died at first, and Burrows did the same,
A pallor wreathed the features of the patrons of the game.
A straggling few got up to go, leaving there the rest,
With that hope which springs eternal within the human breast.
For they thought if only Casey could get a whack at that,
They'd put up even money with Casey at the bat.
But Flynn preceded Casey, and likewise so did Blake.
And the former was a pudding, and the latter was a fake.
So on that stricken multitude a death-like silence sat,
For there seemed but little chance of Casey's getting to the bat.
But Flynn let drive a single to the wonderment of all,
And the much despised Blakey tore the cover off the ball.

And when the dust had lifted and they saw what had oc-
curred,
There was pride in Casey's bearing and a smile on Casey's
face.There was Blakey safe on second, and Flynn was a-
hugging third.
Then from the gladdened multitude went up a joyous yell,
It bounded from the mountain top and rattled in the dell.
For Casey, mighty Casey, was advancing to the bat.
There was ease in Casey's manner as he stepped into his
And when responding to the cheers he lightly doffed his
hat,
No stranger in the crowd could doubt, 'twas Casey at the
bat.
Ten thousand eyes were on him as he rubbed his hands with
dirt,
Five thousand tongues applauded as he wiped them on his
shirt.
And while the writhing pitcher ground the ball into his hip,
Defiance gleamed from Casey's eyes–and a sneer curled
Casey's lip.
And now the leather-covered sphere came hurtling through
the air,
And Casey stood a-watching it in haughty grandeur there;
Close by the sturdy batsman the ball unheeded sped-
"That ain't my style," said Casey–"Strike one," the Umpire
said.
From the bleachers black with people there rose a sullen
roar,
"Kill him! kill the umpire!" shouted some one from the
stand.
And it's likely they'd have done it had not Casey Raised his
hand.
With a smile of Christian charity great Casey's visage
shone,
He stilled the rising tumult and he bade the game go on;

He signaled to the pitcher and again the spheroid flew,
But Casey still ignored it and the Umpire said "Strike two."
"Fraud!" yelled the maddened thousands, and the echo answered "Fraud."
But one scornful look from Casey and the audience was awed.
They saw his face grow stern and cold; they say his muscles strain,
And they knew that Casey would not let that ball go by again.
That sneer is gone from Casey's lip; His teeth are clenched with hate.
He pounds with cruel violence his bat upon the plate;
And now the pitcher holds the ball and now he lets it go,
And the air is shattered by the force of Casey's blow.
Oh! somewhere in this favored land the sun is shining bright,
The band is playing somewhere, and somewhere hearts are light.
And somewhere men are laughing, and somewhere children shout;
But there is no joy in Mudville-mighty Casey has "Struck out."

# The story behind Casey at the bat

**by R.J. Brown**

When George Hearst decided to run for senator from California in 1885 he realized the need of an influential organ, and bought the *San Francisco Examiner* to promote his political ambitions. After the campaign, he presented it to his son, William Randolph Hearst, who had just graduated from Harvard College. While in college the younger Hearst had been editor of the *Harvard Lampoon.*

Hearst brought along with him three members of the *Lampoon* staff to California, including reporter Ernest L. Thayer. Thayer's nickname was "Phin." He wrote a humorous column on a regular basis for the "Examiner" and signed his columns with his nickname.

In the spring of 1888, Thayer wrote *Casey* and submitted it for publication. It appeared in the *Examiner* in the June 3, 1888 edition and was signed "Phin" as usual. When *Casey* made its first appearance, nobody hailed it with shouts of joy or suspected that it would become immortal. A few weeks later, (exact date unknown) the New York *Sun* published the last 8 stanzas of the poem–but signed its author as "Anon." Other than the "Sun," it was just plain ignored by the public.

To become immortal, everyone (or thing) needs a press agent. Archibald Clavering Gunter, an author of novels, was "Casey's" press agent. Always on the look out for incidents to base some of his novels on, Gunter, living in New York, sought and actively read newspapers from around the country on a regular basis. When he read *Casey* for the first time, he clipped it out to save. He wasn't sure just what he would do with it, but he clipped and saved it anyway.

Many weeks later, in August of 1888, Gunter read that both the New York and Chicago baseball clubs would be attending the performance of the comedian De Wolf Hopper at the Wallack Theater in New York. Upon reading the announcement, Gunter instantly knew what he wanted to do with the clipping of *Casey* he had saved.

Gunter approached Hopper, a good friend, and offered the poem for him to recite as he felt the baseball teams would enjoy a comic baseball recitation. Hopper agreed and recited it that night. The rest, as they say, is history. From that point forward in time, *Casey* become immortal–while a good poem to begin with, it took a recital before a group of "famous" baseball players by a professional comedian to bring it to life.

After reviews for Hopper's performance were published, three people came forward to claim authorship and demanded Hopper pay a royalty to use "their" poem. None could prove authorship, so Hopper kept it in his repertory.

Four or five years later, Thayer, living in Worcester, Massachusetts at the time, attended a performance of Hopper in Worcester. After the show, Thayer sent a note backstage requesting to meet Hopper. Thayer gave him the rights to perform it without paying any royalties.

Hopper then proceeded to read the poem some 10,000 times!

*(Article reprinted with permission of R.J. Brown. It originally appeared in Collectible Newspapers, Volume 8, Number 5, October, 1991. Brown is a member of the Newspaper Collectors Society. For more information see the website, www.historybuff.com.)*

# Casey's revenge

**by Grantland Rice**

There were saddened hearts in Mudville for a week or even
more;
There were muttered oaths and curses—every fan in town
was sore.
"Just think," said one, "how soft it looked with Casey at the
bat,
And then to think he'd go and spring a bush league trick
like that!"

All his past fame was forgotten—he was now a hopeless
"shine."
They called him "Strike-Out Casey," from the mayor down
the line;
And as he came to bat each day his bosom heaved a sigh,
While a look of hopeless fury shone in mighty Casey's eye.

He pondered in the days gone by that he had been their

king,
That when he strolled up to the plate they made the wel-
coming ring;
But now his nerve had vanished, for when he heard them
hoot
He "fanned" or "popped out" daily, like some minor league
recruit.

He soon began to sulk and loaf, his batting eye went lame;
No home runs on the score card now were chalked against
his name;
The fans without exception gave the manager no peace,
For one and all kept clamoring for Casey's quick release.

The Mudville squad began to slump, the team was in the
air;
Their playing went from bad to worse—nobody seemed to
care.
"Back to the woods with Casey!" was the cry from Rooters' Row.
"Get some one who can hit the ball, and let that big dub
go!"

The lane is long, some one has said, that never turns again,
And Fate, though fickle, often gives another chance to me;
And Casey smiled; his rugged face no longer wore a
frown—
The pitcher who had started all the trouble came to town.

All Mudville had assembled—ten thousand fans had come
To see the twirler who had put big Casey on the bum;
And when he stopped into the box, the multitude went
wild;
He doffed his cap in proud disdain, but Casey only smiled.

"Play ball!" the umpire's voice rang out, and then the game
began.
But in that throng of thousands there was not a single fan
Who thought that Mudville had a chance, and with the
setting sun
Their hopes sank low–the rival team was leading "four to
one."

The last half of the ninth came round, with no change in
the score;
But when the first man up hit safe, the crowd began to roar;
The din increased, the echo of ten thousand shouts was
heard
When the pitcher hit the second and gave "four balls" to
the third.

Three men on base–nobody out–three runs to tie the game!
A triple meant the highest niche in Mudville's hall of fame;
But here the rally ended and the gloom was deep as night,
When the fourth one "fouled to catcher" and the fifth "flew
out to right."

A dismal groan in chorus came; a scrowl was on each face
When Casey walked up, bat in hand, and slowly took his
place;
His bloodshot eyes in fury gleamed, his teeth were
clenched in hate;
He gave his cap a vicious hook and pounded on the plate.

But fame is fleeting as the wind and glory fades away;
There were no wild and woolly cheers, no glad acclaim this
day;
They hissed and groaned and hooted as they clamored:
"Strike him out!"
But Casey gave no outward sign that he had heard this

shout.

The pitcher smiled and cut one loose—across the plate it
sped;
Another hiss, another groan. "Strike one!" The umpire said.
Zip! Like a shot the second curve broke just below the
knee.
"Strike two!" the umpire roared aloud; but Casey made no
plea.

No roasting for the umpire now—his was an easy lot;
But here the pitcher whirled again—was that a rifle shot?
A whack, a crack, and out through the space the leather
pellet flew,
A blot against the distant sky, a speck against the blue.

Above the fence in center field in rapid whirling flight
The sphere sailed on—the blot grew dim and then was lost
to sight.
Ten thousand hats were thrown in air, ten thousand threw a
fit,
But no one ever found the ball that mighty Casey hit.

O, somewhere in this favored land dark clouds may hide
the sun,
And somewhere bands no longer play and children have no
fun!
And somewhere over blighted lives there hangs a heavy
pall,
But Mudville hearts are happy now, for Casey hit the ball.

*(Reprinted from Base-Ball Ballads, 1910.)*

# Opportunity lost

**by W.C. Madden**

Many good players sometimes don't get much of an opportunity to make it in the majors. One of those unfortunate souls was a player by the name of Mike Sember.

Growing up in Hammond, Indiana, Sember attended a Catholic high school and concentrated on playing football and basketball. Then in his senior year he decided to try out for baseball. He became the starting shortstop for the team and was named as the most valuable athlete in the school by graduation time.

"It was my intention to be a football player and play just enough to get a college scholarship with no intention of playing in the NFL," he explained. However, he changed his mind and attended Tulsa University on an academic scholarship. He liked the school because they allowed him to play more than one sport.

In his freshman year, he tried out for the baseball team and didn't make the cut. "I was demoralized because now I had to go to spring football." Then the baseball coach called him up and asked him to come out, because he had cut too many players.

He made the team as a utility player. Tulsa had a
great team and went to the College World Series, finishing
second. It was a great thrill for him.

After his senior year, the Chicago Cubs picked him
in the second round. He signed for $40,000 and was as-
signed to Class AA Midland, Texas in 1974.

By 1977, he had advanced to the major league
spring training camp and was put on the Cubs 40-man
roster. Sember got cut just before camp broke and was
assigned to Triple-A Witchita.

When backup Mick Kelleher broke a finger in
August that year, Sember was called up. The same day he
got the call, his wife, a flight attendant, was reassigned
from New York to Chicago. Good timing. He struck out in
his first at bat with the Cubs, but he singled in a pinch-
hitting role some games later against San Francisco. He
stayed up with the Cubs the rest of the season, but appeared
in only three games.

In 1978, Sember didn't get the call from the Cubs
until the end of the season. "What happened is that the
Cubs whole starting infield, outfield and catcher came from
somewhere else. The only thing we had that was home
grown was the pitching staff. All the guys that were having
good minor league development had nowhere to go," he
explained.

The following year he was the old man out after
spring training. He asked the Cubs to trade him or release
him. The Cubs put him on waivers and the Toronto Blue
Jays picked him up. He was assigned to Triple-A. He
wasn't used much there becasue he was a new player in the
system, so he retired from baseball.

While Sember had an unfortunate career in the
majors, he has done well for himself and now lives in a big
house with a pool in Florida. Maybe it was all for the best
after all that he didn't become a successful major leaguer.

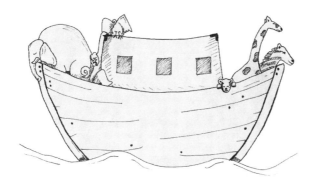

# The first official line-up

**Author unknown**

Eve stole first, and Adam second;
Ruth in the field won fame.
Goliath was struck out by David,
And Abel made a base hit on Cain.
The prodigal son made one home run,
And Noah gave out rain checks.

**Dizzy Dean**

# The Gashouse Gang

**by David S. Montfort**

*(Editor's Note: The St. Louis Cardinals of the 1930s were called The Gashouse Gang, especially the 1934 squad, which went 95-58 and won the World Series. The team was so named because the players got their uniforms so dirty that they resembled the gas company workers in the 1930s. They were a rowdy, passionate team.)*

Even though he was spotted by the Anderson twins, known for tormenting boys at the middle school, Jimmy knew he had no time to take the long way around to avoid them. With a burst of speed and courage, he flew past before the cute little girls could react. He peddled down the dusty side road, jumping the curb and landing on the town's newly bricked Main Street.

The boy's speed was tremendous and seemed to increase with every push of the pedal on his large bright red

Schwinn bicycle with chrome handlebars. Hanging on the right side of handlebars was his baseball glove that swayed and bounced with every movement. Across the entire length of the handlebars was his baseball bat. The red Cardinal baseball cap, which was worn by the Gashouse Gang he loved so much, was pulled tightly down over his head to keep the wind from ripping it off. He swerved around people, between cars and through narrow openings in carefully trimmed bushes.

Jimmy zipped by two old men on the park bench who were feeding the pigeons. The pigeons scattered. One of the men lifted his cane and shook it at him. The man yelled, "Young whippersnapper!"

The young boy was now past the city limits and heading for a shortcut through the woods. He traveled a narrow, winding pathway over the hill and through the creek until he flew over an embankment and on to the dirty highway leading to Sikeston. He soon arrived at Graber's General Store and Gas Station, which featured two new bubble topped Texaco gas pumps. Sitting at the pumps was a shiny black 1929 Stutz. He paid no attention to its driver and went inside the station.

Jimmy put a dime in the new Coke machine and slid out a cold pop. He spotted old man Graber and two other men in the corner of the store fidgeting with the back of the large radio. No sound was coming from the device. He glanced at the clock on the wall. Time was running short.

The driver of the Stutz honked for service. "Jimmy, can you pump gas?" one of the helpers said.

"No, he cain't pump gas," said Graber. "Only I can pump gas. It takes practice."

"Maybe the driver can pump gas?"

"That'll be the day when the customer has to pump his own gas," Graber said. They laughed.

Suddenly, the tube came to life and a voice came out of the speakers of the huge machine. Graber turned knob to get to the right station. "You passed it! Slow down!

The man who had beeped his horn came into the store. "Hey, can I get some gas?"

"Just as soon as I get the Cardinals on the radio."

"I think Dizzy Dean's pitching today," he added.

He was met with the sound of hushes as Graber landed on the right station. The starting lineups were being given. The people in the store had all been drawn together by the magic of the Gashouse Gang in 1934.

Billy Smith was the 65-year-old manager of the St. Louis Cardinals for the 2003 season, but not for long, according to the newspapers. The Cardinals had dropped to the cellar of the Eastern Division, but the most disturbing fact was that the players acted as though they didn't care any more.

After a fifth loss, the players walked lifelessly into the dressing room. One or two gloves were thrown against the lockers, but that was all. Some players were already joking and talking to each other about their nightly plans for partying. Over in another corner, Jim Hatcher, the losing pitcher and considered the team's ace, had just lost his third straight game. "If Willie had dove for that one ball, I have picked up the win!" he yelled to nobody in particular.

The black shortstop looked up with hatred in his eyes. "You son of a bitch!"

Both men began throwing punches. Teammates quickly came to break up the fracas. Then the manager entered. Billy tried to get everyone's attention, but the players continued doing what they were doing. One of the coaches threw a chair against the empty row of lockers to finally get everyone's attention.

Billy leered at John Jarvis, the center fielder. "You got tagged out at third because you didn't slide. Tell me why you didn't slide."

Jarvis looked around, smiled and popped open a beer. "Maybe you didn't get the memo. My agent got it put into my contract that if I'm not the tying or go-ahead run, I don't have to slide."

Billy gave him a questioning look then gazed back to his coach. The coach gave Billy a nod. "I thought you knew?"

The old manager turned back to Jarvis. "It's in your contract not to slide? Now I've heard it all."

Billy shook his head then looked to his losing pitcher, who was recovering from a punch in his ear. "I called for a fastball to Fisher and you threw him a slider that hung. Can you tell me why you didn't throw the fastball?"

"Hey, I got him out, didn't I?" Hatcher replied.

"Yeah, you got him. He flew out 395 feet to center to sacrifice the go-ahead run. He's a sucker for up and hard stuff. I was trying to get a strike out! From now on you go by what I call."

Hatcher turned to his locker in disgust.

Billy knew deep down that he had to say something positive to leave the room in a better air.

"You know fellas, I remember back in '64 when Boyer—"

"Who?"

Billy became disgusted himself and went to his office. The players knew what he was trying to do, but they seemed more interested in leaving than in listening to him.

The next morning, Billy was called to the General Manager's office.

"Billy, people are saying you've lost contact with your players," the GM said.

"You mean the players are talking and you don't mean contact, you mean respect," Billy said.

"I mean you're too old," the general manager explained. "You talk too much about the old days when players were players, and men were men. It's a high-tech game now, Billy. baseball is not the national pastime any more. It's about making money. That's what we've got to do. We have to draw people to see the Cardinals play and that's not going to happen if we're in last place."

"I know, but it's early in the season. I know I can turn this team around," Billy assured him.

"You've got a week or you can start collecting Social Security!"

"Yes, sir."

Billy had been in professional baseball for more than forty-five years. He had played against the best and been with the best, but most of them were gone. He didn't want to go fish and hunt like a lot of his old buddies.

That night he sat on the edge of his bed and prayed: "I've lived a clean life. I've tried very hard to make them understand what the game's really about. For that, I can't see how I have failed. I just want to go out with a peace of mind that my players tried hard for me. That's all." He then turned to the gold-framed photo of his wife, who had passed away a year before, and said, "It's been a heck of a day, Mary."

That night as Billy slept, a strange wind gently blew the curtains and entered his room He always slept with the windows open as he liked fresh air. He began to dream about a mysterious old man watching him. In another part of the dream, he and his coach were digging up buried treasure or something. He couldn't tell. The surroundings looked familiar, but he couldn't place it. Then he awoke. He went over to the open window and looked down on the street. Under the soft amber glow of the street light, an old man stood looking up at him. It was the old man in the dream. He wore an old and tattered overcoat and a hat that was pulled down slight over his face. The old man turned and limped out of sight with the help of a cane.

Billy hurriedly put on his clothes and hurried out to his shed in the backyard. He grabbed two shovels and put them in the back end of his green van. Then called his first base coach on the car phone to help him find the old man and dig up the "treasure." Earl thought Billy was nuts and seeing ghosts, but he agreed to help him out.

The field manager drove to the site of the old baseball stadium because he remembered seeing it in his dream. As they drove up to the site of old Sportsman's Park, they both spotted the old man standing by the swings. He quickly disappeared into the night.

"Grab the shovels," Billy ordered. "We have to dig over where he was standing."

"Billy, what are we doing here?" questioned Earl. "We've done a lot of crazy things together, but this takes the cake. We could be arrested!

"Trust me on this. I saw it in my dream."

"Okay, whatever you say, skipper."

For the next hour the two overweight coaches dug down past the dirt and loose brick. A city police car came by and both men scrambled down into the large hole they had just dug. The police didn't see them.

"Billy, I'm out of here!"

"Come on Earl, just a little more."

"No way, I can't afford to be thrown in jail at my age."

Out of frustration, Billy slammed his shovel down into the hole. It made a sound like it had hit wood.

"Hell! You've hit a casket! It's Hoffa, I knew it. We're in deep now."

"Hoffa's buried in New Jersey, not here."

Billy brushed away the dirt.

"Look!"

Earl flashed the light in the hole and it revealed the top of a traveling trunk. The old logo of the Saint Louis Cardinals was evident.

The two men dug for another 30 minutes and uncovered yet another trunk. After they got one of the trunks out of the hole, they opened it to discover baseball uniforms. "These are the uniforms of the old Gashouse Gang," Billy said.

"What are we going to do with them?" Earl questioned.

"I have an idea. Let's get them into my van and get out of here."

"I'll go along with that."

When the players came into the locker room that morning, they found their brightly colored white and red uniforms replaced by old baggy woolen uniforms. Players held out the old relics of the past and laughed at them. They also laughed at the gloves and bats that were placed in a plastic trash can in the center of the dressing room.

Billy walked out of his office to greet them. "Get used to them, boys. This is your gear for the rest of the season."

Laughter turned to seriousness. "I don't know about the rest of you," said Willie. "But I ain't wearing no crap like this. I've got an image to live up to."

Many of the players agreed with Willie. "I'm calling my agent!" Willie announced.

"Go ahead. It won't do you any good. Your contracts won't help you. I know, I checked. Get your new uniforms on and get out to the field. You've got 10 minutes!"

A couple of minutes later, Billy's phone rang. It was

the general manager's secretary and he was to see the GM now.

"Just what the hell are you trying to do with my team!" yelled the young executive. "We're already in last. Now you want to make us the laughing stock of the entire league."

"You gave me a week, right?"

"Yeah."

"If this doesn't turn the team around, you can have my head," Billy said, gesturing his head being cut off. "Everyone loves an old-time uniform game, so announce that tomorrow's game will be one to honor the Gashouse Gang. People will come. Trust me!"

"Okay, but if the people don't come and we don't win, you'll be out of a job sooner than next week."

"Deal!"

Most of the players grumbled as they donned the uniforms. The hats were tight, the pants were baggy and the gloves were small. The coaches had to show the players how to catch the ball. "You gotta use two hands," said Billy. "Just put in your minds that the glove is for stopping the ball. Your other hand is for holding it in the pocket. With these gloves you have to catch the ball in the palm of your hand."

The players had trouble with the gloves at first, but they began to catch on. No more one handed grabs.

Around the hitting cage, the players had trouble swinging the heavy bats. "Using these bats, you must go for contact instead of swinging for the fences," Billy told his players.

Again, the players had trouble at first, but then they began to catch on.

As practice came to an end, Billy noticed the old man in the left field bleachers. As soon as he began to walk toward him, the old man left down the tunnel. Billy wondered who he could be.

The next day, the press had picked up on the old uniforms and the team got a lot more publicity than they could have ever planned on getting. The stories were blown out of proportion because of complaints by the players. Curious fans poured into the stadium like the team was giving away money.

As the players dressed for the game, Billy approached his starting pitcher. "Hatcher, do you know whose uniform you've got on?"

"No."

"You've got the uniform of a player who was considered the best pitcher in baseball in the 1930s. He had a choice of playing baseball for $7,000 a year or picking cotton for two dollars a week," Billy explained. "But he didn't play for the money. He played for the game. And that's all I've ever asked of you."

"So, who wore this uniform."

"Dizzy Dean."

"Who wore my uniform, coach?" another player asked.

"That was Ducky Medwick's. He was a great clutch hitter."

The players started to feel a little better about the uniforms once Billy told them who they represented.

In a meeting before the game, Billy told them, "The uniforms that you wear are the original uniforms worn by the Gashouse Gang. They were winners and I think you can be, too. Wear them with pride!"

The players yelled and stormed out of the locker room like football players.

By the time the game started, the place was packed.

Hatcher had a three-hitter going to the bottom of the

seventh when a fly was hit in the left-center gap. Jaris got there in time, but dropped the ball trying to make a one-handed stab at the ball. The error cost a run and the Mets went up 1-0.

Going into the bottom of the ninth, the Cardinals were still down by the same score. The first two batters went down in order. Fans started heading to the exits in droves. But Willie walked and so did Jarvis. Hatcher then squirted one off the end of the bat to reach first safely and load the bags. The fans quit leaving and began to yell to urge on the team.

Hatcher turned to Jarvis, who then looked at Willie. All three glanced to each other as though a mental message was being passed back and forth. With the next pitch, Jarvis took a couple of extra steps toward third to get the catcher's attention. No throw. Then the next pitch, Jarvis did the same but fell down. The catcher raised and fired a perfect strike to second base. Willie took off for home. The second baseman fired the ball back to the catcher. The throw was off and Willie scored. The catcher then threw to third to try and catch Jarvis. The ball ricocheted off the third baseman's leg and into foul territory. Jarvis kept running and scored the winning run. The Cardinals had pulled off an improbable double steal to win the game.

Billy turned to Earl, "That's more like it!"

The pair high fived it and jogged out to the field to congratulate the Willie and Jarvis. Something caught Billy's attention in the stand. Sure enough, it was the old man again standing there. As soon as Billy looked at him, he disappeared into the crowd.

In the locker room the players were excited for the first time since the beginning of the season. Reporters asked the players if the play had been planned and they said it had.

The general manager ordered the players to keep

wearing the uniforms and Billy concurred.

As the weeks passed, the team kept winning and moved up the ladder in the standings. The city got behind the team. And the general manager let Billy do anything he wanted. So, he moved the players out of the dugouts and on to benches so they could be closer to the fans, who loved the move. Then a pathway was made from the mound to homeplate like in older times. Old movie clips of the original Gashouse Gang were shown on the big screen before each game. Busch Stadium, now in its last season, was packed for every game. Billy saw fleeting glimpses of the old man during nearly every home game and the team won those games as if he had made the difference.

With two weeks remaining in the season, Billy's players had climbed all the way to challenge the Mets, who were in town for a three-games series. The Cardinals won the first two games and were threatening to sweep the series to take over first place, but the Mets had other ideas and tied the score in the top of the ninth. In the bottom of the ninth, Willie was on first base with two outs. Mitchell took the first two pitches for strikes to put him in a big hole. Billy yelled at him, "Just make contact!"

Mitchell took the manager's advice and choked up. The pitcher wasted two pitches. Then Willie decided he was going to steal second on the next pitch and took off. The ball was down the middle and Mitchell laced a liner to right-center. The ball split the fielders like a field goal and Willie was off to the races. Billy motioned to send him home! The center fielder made a perfect throw to the cutoff man, who turned and fired it home. Everything seemed to magically turn into slow motion so that everyone could follow the path of both projectiles.

When the cloud of dust settled, Willie and the catcher looked to the umpire as did the thousands of fans.

The umpire raised a hand to call Willie out, but then he saw the ball lying on the ground and yelled, "You're safe!"

The place went crazy! The Cardinals were now in sole possession of first place.

The team ended up winning the Eastern Division and going to the World Series to face the New York Yankees. After each team won three games, the final game came down to a contest at Busch Stadium.

As Billy walked to the stadium from his car, the old man he had seen now for months waited by the entrance.

"Who are you?" he asked.

"I'm the man in your dreams," the old man said in a raspy voice. "The Gashouse Gang is proud again. I know, I talk to them all the time."

Billy swallowed hard. "What do you have to do with them?"

Without saying a word, the old man reached into a torn pocket of his overcoat, and pulled out a crumpled photograph of a young boy with Dizzy Dean. "I was their batboy."

"I had no idea."

The old man then pulled out some ancient baseball cards of the Gashouse Gang and showed them to Billy. "They're all my friends, still."

"Okay." Billy didn't know what to say as he looked at the cards. "Do you have a ticket to the game?"

The old man smiled and shook his head from side to side.

"Well, maybe after the game I could buy you a cup of coffee or something," Billy said as he headed into the stadium.

"They're here you know. They've always been here, right beside you."

"I know." Billy turned to get a last glimpse of the old man, but he was gone as if he had disappeared into thin air.

The championship game started off on the wrong
foot for the Cardinals. The Yanks scored two quick runs
and loaded the bases for more. Billy decided to replace his
starter with a young rookie pitcher from Arkansas, because
the Yankees hadn't seen him pitch. Yankee scouts had no
reports on the youngster. The Yankee's manager was almost
panicky on the phone as he tried to find out anything about
the 20-year-old youngster who was called up from the
minors in September.

Billy's strategy paid off. The Yankee hitters had no
idea what was coming. The new pitcher got the Cardinals
out of the jam on a ground ball double play.

The score remained the same until the bottom of the
seventh when Mitchell homered with Jarvis on base to tie
up the game. With the score tied, the young pitcher began
to lose his edge in the top of the ninth. Billy called down to
the bullpen and told Hatcher to warm up. Hatcher was as
surprised as the stopper on the team, because he had just
pitched seven innings the day before.

But something happened during his warm-ups.
Hatcher suddenly started using an old windmill wind-up
style that was used in the thirties.

An old reporter opened his mouth in awe. "My God,
he looks just like Dizzy Dean!" he told a younger reporter
next to him.

Billy brought in Hatcher with the bases loaded full
of Yankees. Using the old wind-up style and double pump,
Hatcher threw three straight strikes to get the Cardinals out
of the jam, much to the amazement of the hitter and the
crowd, which had never seen such an exhibit.

In the bottom of the ninth after an out was made,
Jarvis hit a grounder deep in the hole at short. As he ran
down the line, he could see that the throw was off and the
first baseman had to jump for it. So he slid head first into

the bag to avoid the tag. "Safe!" the umpire yelled. Jarvis called time to wipe the dirt from his face. The crowd cheered his effort.

Billy decided to send Jarvis to get him into scoring position. With the second pitch, Jarvis was off and running. The throw was late. Jarvis was called safe.

The Yankee pitcher then decided to walk the batter to bring up a double-play possibility. Mitchell came up to bat. He worked the count to 3-2. The next pitch was a fastball down the middle that he laced up the middle. Jarvis was sent home as he rounded third. Both the ball and Jarvis met a homeplate at the same time. The Yankee catcher lowered his shoulder and flipped Jarvis into the air. As he did, the ball popped out, but Jarvis had been thrown over homeplate and hadn't touched the bag yet. The catcher scrambled for the ball and Jarvis crawled to the plate like a solder crawling on the ground. They met in a photo finish. "Your safe!" the umpire yelled.

The place went into hysteria! The Cardinals met in the middle of the field to carry off Mitchell, who had the winning hit. Then they turned to Billy and did the same. Thousands of spectators threw their straw hats in the air and some came sailing on to the field.

The team celebrated the victory in the locker room with a sea of champagne. After the celebration was over and the press gone, Billy headed down the darkened corridor himself heading for home. He saw four players sitting on a bench. "Hey fellas, why aren't you inside celebrating with the rest of the team?"

The player closest to him stood up. It was none other than Dizzy Dean. Billy couldn't believe his eyes. The other players introduced themselves. They were Pepper Martin, Terry Moore and Frankie Frishe. "You've done good her, Billy. You put the pride back in the game, and you made the boys realize that baseball is a way of life.

You made them smell the grass again. Now are you ready to come with us?"

"I can't go with you, I plan on managing again next year," Billy replied.

"I'm sorry, but you're time is done here."

Billy heard Mitchell yell out from the locker room. "Quick, someone get a doctor! I think Billy's had a heart attack!"

Then Billy knew why the Gashouse Gang was there.

"Come on, Billy. Mary's waiting for you," Moore said.

Billy and the players disappeared down the corridor.

*(This condensed story is being turned into a major motion picture by Family Motion Pictures at www.familymotionpictures.com. Montfort is a former scout of the Chicago Cubs. He has dedicated this story to Ray Blades, who managed the Cardinals from 1939-40.)*

# First practice

**by Andrea Blaha**

The smell of new leather
The smack of the ball in the pocket
The sting of a hit off an aluminum bat
The wet, spongy ground leaving its imprint on jeans and
knees
A disorganized, but knowing, group of kids trying to be a
team
An organized, but unsure group of men trying to be coaches
The thud, thud, thud of a basketball replaced by the slower
rhythm of a catch
Squirming and fussing getting used to intimate protective
wear
Dormant muscles straining to make the play
Learning to be more interested in what the coach is saying
than the butterfly fluttering by
Pushing and shoving in an ancient male ritual of accep-
tance

*(Blaha is a freelance writer from Bowling Green, Ohio.)*

# Spring training

**by John Robert McFarland**

Feb. 20, 1990. The pitchers and catchers are to report today, the early birds of spring training. Instead, they are locked out by the owners, and I am locked out by the cancer.

When I was a kid, I played in the Church League in Oakland City, Indiana, the hometown of Edd Roush, the Red's Hall of Fame center fielder. His twin brother, Fred, was one of our coaches. Edd used to come out to watch us. He'd get so disgusted he'd grab a bat and start showing us how it was done. He could hit line drives all day. We thought he was fantastic for such an old guy. He was about the age then that I am now.

My grandfather's brother, Rufus, grew up with Edd and Fred. They moved up the ranks of baseball together. They assumed they would go to the majors together. At five-foot-three, Uncle Rufus would have been the smallest man to ever play in the bigs, save for Veeck's midget. Uncle Rufus was a true shortstop, in every sense of the word. Unfortunately he remained one rank short. That left it to me to be the first McFarland to go all the way to Crosley Field, to play the Braves in Boston and the Dodgers in Brooklyn and the Giants in New York.

But I wouldn't be an outfielder like Edd, or a shortstop like Uncle Rufus. I wanted to be in on every pitch, but I was smart enough to avoid the "tools of ignorance." I wanted to pitch. Not just because the pitcher is the focus of the game, standing high and lifted up in the middle of the diamond, but because the pitchers get to go to spring training early.

Edd didn't like spring training. He held out every year, stayed home in Oakland City, not really for the extra money, he always claimed, but so he wouldn1t have to go to Florida in the spring. It's interesting that in his retirement, he spent half of every year in Florida, lived within a line drive of the Reds' spring training camp.

I couldn't understand Edd. February is mostly chilly and damp in southern Indiana. Even though we plant our leaf lettuce on Valentine's Day, there's no spring there then. Edd must have been crazy not to want to go to spring training. I wanted to be in the land of grapefruit on the very first day of spring training, working out with Ed Bailey and Ewell "The Whip" Blackwell. No waiting until the outfielders and shortstops got there for me.

Alas, although I had great control, I learned that control without speed, movement, or deception is primarily an invitation to the long ball. I was weak of arm, slow of foot, and swung the heaviest bat in the Church League, just like Edd Roush swung the heaviest bat in the majors. I was also six foot and an inch, had an arm span a stork would envy, and could catch the ball every time. Catching the ball was not an automatic in the Church League. All that, of course, meant I was assigned to first base.

We lived three miles out in the country. We had no car. I

had to hike it back and forth for every practice and every game. Younger people automatically cringe whenever oldsters start telling of those long walks "when we were kids." I remember those walks as a skip and a hop, with maybe a jump thrown in. They were simply a way to get to where I could play ball. Those walks weren't sacrifices or hardships. Three miles? That's nothing when there is a diamond at the end of the road.

There was one problem with living in the boon-docks, though. We attended a country church, Forsythe Methodist. It was too small to field a team in the Church League. I had to get special dispensation from the commis-sioner of baseball to play with the town Methodists. When I heard that, I had visions of meeting Happy Chandler. The commissioner, however, turned out to be a local auto mechanic. After careful questioning to be sure I wasn't really a heathen who just wanted to play ball, he gave me the necessary clearance. Frankly, I thought heathen should be allowed to play, too. What better evangelism could there be? Nonetheless, I was immensely proud of the small, felt, green "M" that I got to wear on my white T-shirt.

So, I became the All-Star first bagger for the Meth-odists. Clean-up hitter, too. It was good, playing first base, but I realized I would have to wait and go to spring training with the "other" players.

I never made it to the bigs. I never even made it to spring training, but I licked the cancer that took a third of my colon.

*(McFarland is a member of the Society for American Baseball Research and author of "Now That I Have Can-cer I Am Whole: Meditations for Cancer Patients and Those Who Love Them.")*

**Lou Gehrig**

# You know you're a baseball fan when...

**by W.C. Madden**

The Lou Gehrig Story makes you cry.
A full count makes your mouth dry.
You still own your Little League mitt.
You can recall your first ever hit.
The National Anthem gives you a chill.
Hitting a grand slam was your biggest thrill.
You can't wait for the umpire to say, "Play ball!"
A player steals second and you make the call.
You go to see the last-place team play.
You can sit through a two-hour rain delay.
Take Me Out to the Ball Game is your favorite song.

You think the umpire is always wrong.
A hot dog and beer is your favorite meal.
You feel a season ticket is the best deal.
You always keep the score.
The game is over and you want more

**Johnny Podres**

# A special birthday

**by Phil Jacobsen**

The Chinese calendar uses animals to mark the passage of time: the year of the horse, the year of the rat, the year of the snake, etc. If you're into astrology you could be a crab, a lion, a fish or some other item you might find on the back of a tarot card. But I was born into an all-American family. We didn't use fantasy mumbo-jumbo to determine our biorhythms. We marked time by baseball–by the World Series specifically.

My dad was born in the year of the St. Louis Cardinals. The year Stan "The Man" Musial and George "Whitey" Kurowski were rookies. The year the Cardinals humbled the New York Yankees, winning the World Series four games to one. If your life is not measured by baseball, that was 1942.

Twenty-five years later, 1967, I was also born in the year of the St. Louis Cardinals. In 1967 the Cardinals didn't have quite the cakewalk they did in '42. In '67, the Boston

Red Sox pushed the Cardinals into a seven-game series. With Bob Gibson pitching, the Cardinals won the World Series in the seventh game, 7-2. Because my dad and I were both born in the year of the Cardinals, we have a lot in common. Our personality types are the same; we share the same alma mater; our careers are similar; and, my middle name is his name, too. A chip off the old block? There is one big difference though: growing up, I didn't like baseball and baseball didn't like me.

I would have rather admitted to my father I didn't believe in God than I would want to say I didn't believe in baseball. At least with God, there was room for theological or philosophical debate. Does God exist? What does one hand sound like when it claps? Quite simply, my dad and I had two different experiences growing up with baseball.

It seems like the "heydays" of baseball have passed. And they passed right in front of my father's eyes. The first World Series he can remember was in 1947. The New York Yankees played the Brooklyn Dodgers, and it came down to the seventh game. The Dodgers scored two runs in the top of the second, putting them ahead 2-0. Those would be the only runs the Dodgers would get in the rest of the game. The Yankees won 5-2.

My grandfather was a Yankees fan, born in the year of the last time the Boston Red Sox won the Series, which was 1918. When the Yankees won, my dad became a Brooklyn Dodgers fan. In 1949, the Yankees beat Brooklyn 4 games to 1. In 1952, New York beat Brooklyn 4 games to 3. In '53, 4 games to 2. 1955 was a different story.

In 1955 my father was 13 years old. He was playing baseball in the parking lot across the street from his house in Vernal, Utah. He was the first kid in his neighborhood to hit a home run over the rodeo grandstands, and he was still a Brooklyn Dodgers fan.

My dad was one of the boys of summer. By then, he

was more than a fan. He could rattle off statistics with abbreviations and match them up to player and position–ERAs, RBIs and HRs to Johnny Podres, Jackie Robinson and Duke Snider.

Everything about this 1955 team said this was the year they would win the World Series. They had the bats, the arms and the gloves. What they didn't have was history. So, when the series became tied at three apiece, it looked like another year for the Yankees. "Looked" is the operative word and Johnny Podres was the operative player. The Dodgers again only scored two runs in the seventh game like the '47 team. But, since Podres pitched a scoreless game, those two runs made 1955 the Year of the Brooklyn Dodgers. The only year that Brooklyn ever won the World Series.

I don't know why he gravitated toward the Brooklyn Dodgers. But I know why he gravitated toward baseball. It was his escape. It wasn't a field of dreams, it was a dream that took place on a field. As long as those nine innings were being played the outside world could be in complete chaos, because inside the world of baseball everything was pitcher perfect.

World War II? What Korean War? The Vietnam War was just a conflict. And through it all, baseball played on taking my father, and many other families, away from reality. Baseball took them out to the ballpark. Is it any wonder they didn't care if they ever came back? My version of baseball is not apple pie. Maybe baseball needs patriotism to hang its hat on. Right now it escapes me which teams were playing in the World Series during the U.S. invasion of Grenada and Panama. But I do recall the Oakland A's were dynamite during Watergate.

I still remember my batting average from when I played little league baseball. It's not that I have a good memory, but rather because I never hit the ball. The rest of my statistics were equally unimpressive, except for one–my dad came to 100 percent of my games. Every time I struck out, he told me my swing looked like it was improving. Every time I walked, he would yell, "Good eye! Good eye!" And every time I got hit by the ball, he told me I was "Taking it for the team." And let me tell you, I got hit by the ball a lot.

I know more about 1955 baseball than I do baseball in general. So, in 1997 when my dad was approaching his 55th birthday, I wrote a letter to as many living Brooklyn Dodgers as I could get addresses.

I told them about an obsessed man who drove around California with a license plate that said "1955 Dodger Fan." I told them that 42 years after they stepped off the baseball field, they still had the respect of one man. And he was my dad. I included a self-addressed stamped envelope and then threw out the first pitch to my father's personal World Series. I figured this was going to be a no-hitter. I had no idea what was about to happen.

Fifty letters were sent to men who were my father's heroes. Only 10 of the addresses I had collected came back as "address unknown." But of the 40 letters that did make it to the baseball legends of yesteryear, 33 sent my dad a letter, a card or better.

Within a week of sending out the letters, Ken Lehman, a pitcher for the Brooklyn Dodgers, sent a note on a reissue baseball card that simply said, "Happy Birthday, Doug."

When my dad got this card from Ken Lehman, he couldn't figure out why. So my dad did what he thought he deserved, he called Lehman. Lehman told him about what I had done, and that I wasn't original. He said he's approached all the time for autographs and birthday wishes, and refuses most of them. But somehow the letter from me struck a chord, and he wanted to send a card from his personal collection.

My dad thanked him and said goodbye. But Lehman asked him, "Doug, how often do you get to talk to a Brooklyn Dodger? Why don't you ask me some questions?" For the next 45 minutes my dad asked, Ken talked and that was only the beginning.

Russ Meyer, the ill-tempered pitcher who threw a grand-slam pitch to Mickey Mantle, threw out birthday wishes to my father. One month later, he died.

Elmer Valo sent birthday and Christmas wishes, too. His card was slightly belated. He died seven months later.

Johnny "1955 MVP" Podres sent an autographed 8x10, as did Roger Craig, Bob Aspromonte and Tommy Lasorde.

The pitcher, Danny McDeviff, and the catcher, Joe Pignatano, from the last game at Ebbets Field reunited in 1997 to send birthday wishes and Dodger memorabilia to my father.

I've only seen my father cry twice. Once when his mother died, and once when he thanked me for his birthday gift.

That should be the end of the story, but I wanted to add a footnote. We were both born in the year of the Cardinals, so it seemed appropriate that on July 3, 1999, he throw out the first pitch at Busch Stadium, home of the St. Louis Cardinals, in front of 35,953 people.

*(Doug Jacobsen, Phil's father, is a member of the Society for American Baseball Research.)*

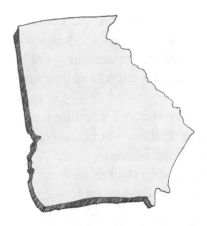

# Ode to a Georgia gent

**by William F. Kirk**

A shudder ran around Forbes Field
    When Tyrus Cobb stole home.
The brain of Honus Wagner reeled
    When Tyrus Cobb stole home.
Manager Clarke his temples clasped,
The Pirate rooters simply gasped–
Their tenderest feelings had been rasped
    When Tyrus Cobb stole home.

The Pirate pitcher's heart stood still
    When Tyrus Cobb stole home.
Gibson, the catcher, had a chill
    When Tyrus Cobb stole home.
Large gobs of smoke began to crawl
Across the ball yard, like a pall,
And gloom was booding over all
    When Tyrus Cobb stole home.

The rooters from Detroit went mad
  When Tyrus Cobb stole home.
A very pleasant time was had
  When Tyrus Cobb stole home.
Small wonder that they shouted so;
In Hughey Jennings's town, we know,
The burglar list is sure to grow
Since Tyrus Cobb stole home.

*(Reprinted from Right Off The Bat, 1910.)*

**Ty Cobb**

# Dreamed I saved Ty Cobb from drowning

**by C. Brooke Rothwell**

Ty and I were walking in the woods
Side by side when suddenly I faced him
Placed my hand on his shoulder
Asked if he'd sign a biography I had of him
He said OK
I said it was a good biography
He acquiesced
I was exhilarated
We neared the bank of a deep gorge
Covered with plush emerald moss
I mentioned how lush it was
Cobb went right for it
Slid down the side and sank straight up underneath
Parting the surface of matted algae
There his almost bald head was visible

My foot stuck in the ground
I yanked it free
Then skied down the bank
Into the water as Cobb slowly sort of bobbed up
Not really moving weirdly calm and far away but alive yet
Visibly pissed
I grabbed him under the arm while reaching for a branch
Yelling for help suddenly concerned about his willingness
Too sign my copy
Of his life story

*(Rothwell is a member of the Society for American Baseball Research.)*

# Playing with heart

**By Bob Bellone**

Tony Saunders rubbed his eyes with his right hand as he tried in vain to force back the tears. His left arm– which for a time had all of baseball rubbing its collective eyes–hung uselessly in a sling.

Until Saunders could regain his composure, the tattoo just above the cast on his pitching arm spoke volumes to reporters on hand to hear him concede his playing days were behind him. "My World" the tattoo declared in script letters above a hand gripping a baseball. "It's so hard knowing you're done," he finally managed to say.

The baseball world of Tony Saunders began to unravel only a few hundred feet from this solemn gathering at Tropicana Field in St. Petersburg, Florida. He was in the third inning of a start for the host Tampa Bay Devil Rays on May 26, 1999.

With two outs and runners at the corners, then-Texas Rangers slugger Juan Gonzalez unknowingly stood in to face a 3-2 pitch that would punctuate Saunders' brief major-league career. Catcher John Flaherty heard a loud snap a split-second before the ball sailed past him to the screen. In front of him, Saunders flopped to the ground and cried out in agony.

He was taken off on a stretcher with a clean spiral break in his left humerus–the large bone that connects the shoulder to the elbow–that left it burning, then numb.

The incident horrified all who had witnessed it.

"I'll never forget it," Flaherty said 15 months later. "I just tried to hold his right hand and let him know we were there until he calmed down a little bit and the trainers got out  there. It was a very emotional moment."

The grisly scene conjured up memories of three other major-leaguers–Dave Dravecky of the San Francisco Giants (1989), Tom Browning of the Cincinnati Reds (1994) and John Smiley of the Cleveland Indians (1997)–whose left arms broke while delivering pitches.

Within an hour of his injury, Saunders' arm was set. So, too, was his mind that he would become the first among them to regain his effectiveness at the big-league level.

"Physically it's going to be tough," he said three days later. "But the mental part of it, there's no doubt about it, that's going to be the hardest part."

So with the help of Devil Rays head trainer Jamie Reed, Saunders picked himself up and went back to work. "I didn't have to push him into anything because he was always at the door, trying to bang through it," Reed said. "Actually, we were cautious a lot of times. He wasn't a happy camper those days. But that's the perfect guy to rehab."

On Aug. 2, 2000, Saunders did what many first thought was unthinkable by returning to a professional mound. In a rehabilitation start for the Charleston RiverDogs of the Class A South Atlantic League, he pitched two scoreless innings against the Augusta (Georgia) Greenjackets. "When I got up on the mound and there was a batter in the box, I said, 'OK, here it is.'"

Saunders reclaimed the first ball he pitched that night and tossed the keepsake to his wife Joyce in the stands. "It represents all my hard work. I worked my butt off this year," he said. "I appreciate this game a lot more. I'm thankful that I am back up there pitching again."

When his workouts brought Saunders back to Tropicana Field, curiosity sometimes got the better of his Tampa Bay teammates.

"There were some days when we watched him throw on the side and we were like, 'Man, this guy might never be the same,'" Devil Rays closer Roberto Hernandez said. "Then there were some days we'd see a glimpse of him coming back."

Saunders was only a matter of days away from being recalled to the majors Aug. 24 when he made his fifth rehabilitation start at Al Lang Field, a dozen blocks from Tropicana Field. Then suddenly, his field of dreams was unreachable. In the third inning of a Class A Florida State League game between the St. Petersburg Devil Rays and Clearwater Phillies, Saunders again broke the arm delivering a pitch.

Eerily, the skies opened up moments after he crumbled to the mound with screams of pain. Players from both teams barely could look at the fallen pitcher as they shielded him and medical personnel from the downpour with a tarp.

Ironically, Saunders' major-league teammates had just arrived in Baltimore—where he was born and a short distance from his home in Severn, Maryland—for a series with the Orioles when they received word of the incident.

"My heart sunk," Reed said. "It was actually much harder to take the second one than the first one because he had done so well."

Saunders' pain may have been more acute two days later as he officially gave up the fight to resurrect his career at age 26. "I can't do it again," he said during an emotional press conference. "I did everything they asked me to do and a little bit more." Saunders' courage and work ethic made a profound impression on players throughout the Tampa Bay organization.

Even Hernandez, who surprised doctors by overcoming a career-threatening arm injury while pitching in the Chicago White Sox system in 1991, was awed by Saunders' willingness to risk a reoccurrence. "It probably would have messed me up mentally, knowing that it might happen again," the right-hander said. "When it turned out that it did, I couldn't believe it happened. People don't understand how much work he put into it. To come back as far as he did, that's just remarkable in itself."

Said Devil Rays outfielder Greg Vaughn: "I always try to tell people this game was here before us, it's going to be here after us. We're not doing it a favor, so appreciate it.

"Play with passion. Play with emotion. Play with heart," Vaughn continued. "Watching Tony going about his business, that was it."

*(Bellone is a freelance writer from Tampa, Florida.)*

# Baseball never out of date

**by S.E. Kiser**

Every year or two they tell us that baseball is out of date;
But each spring it's back in fashion, when they line up at
the plate;
When the good old, glad old feeling comes again to file its
claim,
When a man can turn from trouble and go out to see the
game.
Come, let's sneak away, pretending duty summons us
somewhere,
For out there is happy freedom from men's worries and
their care.
Why consider ages wrinkles or remember old mistakes,
When we may be gloating over the fine plays the home
team makes?

*(Reprinted from Werner's Readings and Recitations, 1916.)*

# America's pastime

**by Joe Boesch**

Yesterday there was Willie, Mickey and the Duke.
Today there is the Rocket, Junior and Big Mac.
Tomorrow there is Bip, John and Steve.

It's not music, but a game that makes its own music.
From the singing of the anthem...
To the crack of the bat.

To the Duke hitting a home run in Ebbets,
Big Mac taking his swing at 70... 80...
Junior going downtown.

Each with something in mind-to win.
America's game-Baseball
The National Pastime.

*(Boesch is a freelance writer from Nesconset, New York.)*

# Mutiny on the diamond

## by W.C. Madden

The South Bend Blue Sox manager penciled in the lineup card for the first game of the championship playoffs, the equivalent of the World Series, against the Rockford Peaches. When Karl Winsch finished with the ninth batter in the order, catcher Wimp Baumgartner, he spit out a wad of tobacco juice on the field next to the freshly painted green wooden dugout. He put the receiver last in the order because she was a poor hitter. He had no alternative. His starting catcher had joined the recent mutiny.

The moon showed its pitted face for the first time through a gap in the clouds in the eastern sky. A few shattered showers danced around the northern Illinois industrial city area during the day, but the rain had missed the field. Now it was a little past 8 p.m. and the sun had given way to its night-time replacement like a pinch hitter late in the game.

The game was being played at Rockford's red-bricked

Beyer Stadium, also affectionately known as the Peach Orchard by the fans. The stadium could seat more than 5,000 in the concrete grandstands. And for one game years earlier, a crowd estimated at more than 10,000 spilled onto the field for a game. Although this was the Women's World Series, a much smaller crowd was expected. The league was no longer packing the stadiums. The novelty of pretty women in short skirts playing baseball had worn off like a bad paint job. The league was now concluding its tenth season in 1952, and it took more publicity and special promotions to bring in the fans.

Attendance had dropped off sharply after the 1948 season when the league was at its zenith with 10 teams. It drew almost a million fans that year. The owners had to promote the game more now with special nights, such as ladies Night or School Days Night. Television was having an impact on the sport. People could watch major league baseball on the television tube in the luxury of their own living rooms. The society was more mobile now that many could afford an automobile. Instead of a baseball game, people could go to the drive-in movie for a double feature, dance at the roadhouse or dine at a restaurant. Women's baseball had a lot of entertainment competition.

The series should have opened in South Bend, because the Sox had finished second in the regular season. But Rockford's stadium was being altered to accommodate high school football after Sunday, so the team's management pleaded to have the series open there first; otherwise, the games would have to be played elsewhere and the team would certainly face financial losses, something it could ill afford to do in these tough times.

About the time Winsch completed the lineup card, his four-year-old son, Larry, was being put to bed by the babysitter back in South Bend. Winsch had to leave his son with a sitter because his wife was pitching the first game of the series. Jean Faut was one of the reasons the team made it into the women's World Series in the first place. The couple carried different last names because Jean began playing under her maiden name before they were married. Some players had changed their name when they married, which caused some confusion. Faut wanted to avoid any mix-ups.

Her league leading record of 20-2 took the team to a second-place finish during the regular season. On top of that, she won one of the games in the first playoff series against the Grand Rapids Chicks. Her .909 winning percentage was a league record and it surpassed the major league record of .880, which was set in 1880 by Fred Goldsmith of Chicago and tied in 1951 by Preacher Roe of the Brooklyn Dodgers.

Some sportswriters and fans were surprised when South Bend won the first round of the playoffs, considering the circumstances. The team had played poorly in August and dropped out of first place with 11 games left in the season. The Sox lost a lot of games it should have won. Some of the players blamed Winsch for the team's troubles. The manager never explained his actions or reasons surrounding what some players thought were strange coaching decisions. He did not feel that he was obliged to justify his actions. He was the manager. He had to make hard decisions. Despite all the problems, he had overcome the odds and took his team to the final series. That is what he was paid to do.

The Peaches had overcome the odds as well in getting to the final playoffs. The team knocked off the pennant-winning, hard-hitting Fort Wayne Daisies in the first round of the playoffs. This was quite an accomplishment because the Daisies led the league with a .257 batting average compared to the Peaches .235. Rockford finished 12 games behind the Daisies in the regular season, so naturally everyone thought the Daisies would win the first round and end up facing the Grand Rapids Chicks in the series. However, in a short series of three games anything could happen, and it did. Rockford's pitching was a little stronger than Fort Wayne's hitting, and that spelled the difference. Rockford also had history on its side. The Peaches captured two pennants and four championships in first nine years of the league. The team was considered the Yankees of the women's league. Fort Wayne had been in the league since 1945 and had never won a championship. This pennant victory had been its first.

South Bend also had a winning tradition in recent times. After doing nothing the first six years in the league, the team won the pennant in 1949. Then Winsch took over as manager in 1951 and guided the team to a pennant and its first championship. In 1952, he guided the team to a second-place finish in the regular season and a sweep of Grand Rapids in the first round of the playoffs.

The stage was now set for the second- and third-place teams during the regular season to face each other for the championship.

The South Bend manager hoped things would go better in the series than it had throughout the season. It was if a black cloud had settled over the team throughout the long, hot summer. Rainouts, injuries, suspensions, protests, ejections and a late-season losing streak had contributed to South Bend's demise. Then came the final blow that ended any chance at the pennant and put an ominous cloud over the playoffs. His job could be at risk as well. Winning a championship would change all that. And Winsch wanted to win it more than any of his players.

The manager became tired of chewing and spit out the remaining tobacco from his mouth. As he waited for the meeting with the umpires at homeplate, his mind drifted off to spring training and the beginning of the troubled season.

The ingredients for the bomb that would explode later

in the season were put together before spring training ever got under way in South Bend. Several players from the 1951 championship team returned their contracts unsigned in early April. They indicated to the Sox management they wanted more of an increase before they would sign. The league standard was $5 a week more than the year before, but these players thought they should get more. A monthly salary cap of $5,400 by the league made increases difficult.

Blue Sox President Bill Sheehan settled the matter in early April by talking to who he thought was the main instigator:

Charlene "Shorty" Pryer. He told her straight out that he was through negotiating salary increases. Pryer was to get $450 a month, the second highest salary on the team behind top pitcher Jean Faut. Pryer finally signed and the rest of the dissenters fell in line.

Sheehan told Dr. Harold Dailey, a member of the Sox beard of directors, about the conversation he had with Pryer. Daily wrote about it in his team diary: "These girls have no idea of loyalty and will sell the team down the line if they don't get back exactly what they want. Some of those girls are Stovroff, Wiley, etc."

Spring training would be held at the club's home field at Playland Park. This was done to help the team hold down expenses. Manager Winsch had three-and-a-half weeks to get his team in playing shape for the season opener at Battle Creek on May 15. He would put his players through two workouts a day, weather permitting.

The weather had turned warm just in time for the first day's activities on April 21, a Monday. In the morning, the women were issued their equipment and uniforms. The players were given two uniforms, a white one for home games and a powder blue for away games, matching bloomers, a hat and a red warm-up jacket. The one-piece uniform was made of a heavy twill for rugged endurance.

The top of the uniform was a tunic, which buttoned down the left-hand side from the waist to the shoulder. The shirt was mid-thigh in length and showed off much of the legs, an attractive feature for the fans but painful for the players who slid into bases. Sliding pads were available, but they helped very little. Many players ended up being bandaged much of the season from the strawberries they would get on their legs from sliding.

After lunch, the women changed into their white uniforms for picture taking by the team photographer and the press that had showed up on the pleasant day. Winsch decided the ground was too wet for any exercising or practicing, so after the photos were taken the players were sent home.

The 1952 camp featured several possible rookies, which were needed to comply with the rookie rule. The rule required a rookie in the defensive lineup at all times. A rookie was considered any player who had played less than five playing months in the league or who played less than 50 games in a season. Pitchers who threw less than 50 innings were given the rookie status. Rookies were determined at the beginning of the season and retained that status for the whole season. Many teams tried to keep rookies in that status for more than a season so they would get experience and still retain the title for another year.

The strategy sometimes backfired as a player would become disgruntled for not getting enough playing time and quit. Winsch used the strategy himself in 1951 when he had played Barbara Hoffman in 49 games. Now he could use her as a rookie again, but she was really a veteran.

The manager used the same tactic with Rose Montalbano. She played in less than 10 games in 1951 and was now more prepared to play regularly. Monty, her nickname, had a scar on her back from a knife wound she received in New York City. The chunky little Italian had silky black hair and a dark complexion.

Besides Hoffman and Montalbano, Winsch had several other rookies in camp, including Mary Froning, Peggy Fenton, Barbara Gates and Toni Nermo. The year before he had looked at two colored women during spring training, but he felt they were not ready to play in the league. The league had not yet broken the color barrier like the majors had done in 1947 when Jackie Robinson began playing. The women's league was more cautious about the decision for whatever reason.

Winsch had 22 players in camp, but he would have to cut down to 17 players by Opening Day. As the general manager of the team as well, he also had to concern himself with salaries and the monthly pay cap imposed by the league. The minimum for a rookie was $55 a week or $220 per month. Veterans were to get a maximum raise of $5 increase per week per year, yet some of the top league players received more money under the table or other incentives secretly from teams in violation of league rules.

Because of the cap on salaries, some players were offered better money to play elsewhere. Several went to the rival Chicago National league. The Sox had lost Audrey Wagner to the National league. Dr. Dailey spoke to her before spring training about returning to the Sox to play. She told him she was happy with the Chicago league and the salary she was getting, which was a litde higher than she would get from the Sox.

Although the league had lost some talent to rival leagues, some good players still existed because the Kenosha Comets and Peoria Redwings had folded after the 1951 season. The players were divvied up to the remaining six teams in the pro league. The Sox drafted Joyce Hill Westerman, Ruby Stephens, Lenora Mandella and Jo Lenard. The acquisitions had cost the Sox $800. Only Mandella and Lenard had reported to spring training. Dr.

Dailey felt Lenard was a poor choice after the draft in March and wrote in his diary: "In fact I will never understand why we took Lenard in the sale as she has been done two years ago." Lenard had been in the league since 1944 and was on the 1946 All-Star Team. She was nicknamed "Bubblegum" because she snuck children into the ballpark in exchange for the pink candy. Then she'd chew it incessantly. The outfielder was sure-handed in the field and a solid hitter. She lacked home run power, yet she had her share of extra-base hits during her days. Plus, she was a veteran player, so she could lend her experience to the rookies.

"Smokey" Mandella, a tall brown-haired woman, was a pitcher who had seen little action in her three years in the league. Her record was 3-4 in 17 games over the past three seasons. Winsch was unsure of her ability. He would give her a try.

The manager could only hope the other players would report. Some players had witnessed the decline of the league over the past three years, so they bailed out for professional softball, college, family life or a job with a lot more security and future. Such was the case with his star shortstop from the 1951 season, Senida "Shoo Shoo" Wirth. She became pregnant in the off-season and left the league to raise a family. Wirth would be missed. She hit a career-best .274, stole 69 bases and knocked in a career-high RBI. She was one of the few rookies ever to be named to an All-Star team.

The Sox also had failed to sign outfielder Pat Crawley to a contract after trading pitcher Sue Kidd for her during the winter. Crawley returned the unsigned contract and said she had a good job as a stewardess for United Airlines. Because Crawley would not sign a contract, the Sox told Kidd not to report to Battle Creek.

On April 24, the failed Crawley/Kidd trade was

heatedly discussed at the league's monthly meeting. Battle
Creek officials felt they should have Kidd because the Sox
had not given Crawley a good offer. Sox President Bill
Sheehan won the battle as the board voted four to one to
nullify the trade. Kidd could stay with the Sox.

A couple of days later, Dr. Dailey offered
Westerman, the draft pick from the defunct Peoria team,
$100 a week to play for the Sox. She told him she would
think about it and give him a response in a week. A week
later she called him back and said she was not interested in
playing for the Sox. That left the Sox without a veteran first
baseman.

The Sox had the same problem at shortstop with
Wirth retiring. Manager Guy Bush of Battle Creek gave the
Sox 24 hours to trade pitcher Sue Kidd and Jetty Vincent
for veteran shortstop Tenny Petras, who the Belles had
picked up in the winter draft from Kenosha. Dr. Daily
discussed the matter with Winsch, who nixed the offer
because he did not want to lose two pitchers for an infielder.

The last day of spring training was a poor day for
practicing. A cloudy, cool day in the 50s greeted the players
at the northern Indiana town not far from the sand dunes of
Lake Michigan. The ground at Playland Park was still as
soggy as a wet sponge from rains the day before. The
infield was a muddy mess. Only the old cinder race track
area behind homeplate provided solid, dry ground for the
players to throw to each other without getting wet.

For the first three weeks of spring training in 1952,
Winsch concentrated on the basics of baseball with the
players. He had several rookies that needed to learn all the
particulars of the game before he could count on them
during the season. A couple of newcomers knew absolutely
nothing about baseball rules. They had been softball players. Getting used to a smaller 10-inch ball and hitting

overhand pitching were two of the biggest hurdles that players had to tackle when coming from the softball field to the baseball diamond. They also had to learn how to steal bases. Winsch relied on his veterans to teach the ropes to the rookies. His expertise was pitching.

Winsch was very knowledgeable about baseball. He had played the game ever since he could lift a bat as a child growing up in East Greenville, Pennsylvania, where he was born of German parents. He worked his way up to semipro ball in Pennsylvania until Jocko Collins signed him to the Philadelphia Phillies farm system. Assigned to Rome, New York, of the Canadian-American League, he was pitching good when he was cut because he was the highest paid player at $250 a month on a team who couldn't afford him. He went back home. Winsch ran into Collins in Philadelphia later and the scout could hardly believe what had happened. So, Collins signed him to another contract and he went to Trenton, New Jersey, to play. Then he was transferred to Utica, New York. The sidearm hurler was finally put on the Phillies roster after spring training one season, but he never got a chance to pitch in the month he was with the team. He was sent back to the minors.

The five-foot-ten-and-a-half, 165-pound right hander pitched well, but not good enough to crack the majors. He gave up professional baseball soon after that and went to work at the Studebaker Plant in South Bend. While he worked at the plant, he continued to play semipro ball, which is how he met his wife, Jean Faut. The Pennsylvania Dutch tomboy had hung around the team like a puppy seeking attention. Winsch took it upon himself to teach her all he knew about pitching. The barnstorming team allowed her to throw batting practice as an added attraction. The two became intimate and married in 1946 after her first season with All-Americans.

Faut began the league as a third baseman for South

Bend. When the league switched to sidearm pitching the next season, she was given a try on the mound and she responded with an 8-3 record. She pitched one marathon game during the season that lasted 23 innings. She continued to improve, but had to take time off in 1948 to deliver the couple's first son. Larry was born on March 30 and Faut missed all of spring training bringing him into the world. The following year she came of age as a pitcher: 24-8 record with a minuscule 1.10 ERA. Then in 1951 she retired 27 Rockford Peaches in a row for a perfect game! She was named to the All-Star Team and became the Player of the Year. Plus, she helped the team to the pennant and championship.

They were a handsome couple. Karl with his short, chestnut brown hair and gray eyes contrasted with Jean's light brunette locks and blue eyes. Both had short hair, but hers was a little longer. She would tuck it behind her ears when she played to get it out of her way. She was a good half-foot shorter than he. They both had large builds from their big bone structures, but neither had much fat on them. Both were attractive, but not overly so. At age 32, he still possessed a boyish face, which was accentuated by his burly eyebrows. On the field it was difficult to tell they were married by the way they acted toward each other. He treated her like any other player, and she acted like any other player.

For the most part, their marriage had been a good one. However, him being the manager and her being a player on the same team sometimes put a strain on their relationship. Many of the players avoided much contact with her because she was the manager's wife.

Earlier in spring training, he had sent her to the showers during practice because she was playing around on the field. He showed no favoritism toward her because she was his wife. The fact remained though and players sometimes treated her like she had leprosy. Jean despised the treatment. She would grin and bear it as best she could.

On Sunday, May 11, the Blue Sox played their first exhibition game for the fans. The intersquad game was held at Centennial Park in South Bend and was sponsored by the Argos and Plymouth Lions Clubs. The team needed as many sponsors as possible to help keep it afloat Sponsors paid hard cash to host games and put fans in the stands, two essentials for the game.

Winsch divided his 22 players into two equal squads and called them the Blues and the Whites, the colors of the team. He assigned three pitchers to each team, so they would each get three innings of work.

The game began at 2:30 p.m. under a patchwork sky reminiscent of the team colors. Several hundred fans showed up on the warm day to see the contest Faut started for the Blues and gave up nothing in the first three innings. Arnold was just as stingy for the Whites. In the fourth inning, Winsch changed pitchers. All-Star second baseman Charlene "Shorty" Pryer tripled and scored to give the Blues the lead until the bottom of the ninth. Blues' hurler Betty Wagoner had control problems and walked in a run to tie the score. The Whites won 2-1 when catcher Wimp Baumgartner let a ball get by her with the bags loaded.

Although it was ugly way to end a game, Baumgartner was not ugly. The farm girl was above average in the look's department. She was muscular and stocky from playing sports all year long. Her dark brown eyes matched her hair. She was the backup catcher to starter Shirley Stovroff. Wimp had seen little action in her first two seasons in the league. She had also spent a year with the traveling teams in 1949 to get more experience. The traveling teams, the Chicago Colleens and Springfield Sallies, existed for two seasons in 1949 and 1950 to give young players like the Hoosier from Fort Wayne more experience. The teams were like the barnstorming teams of the era. They logged thousands of miles in circling the eastern United States and into Canada. When she was on the traveling teams, manager Lenny Zintak converted her from being an outfielder to a catcher. He thought she was too slow for the outfield. The passed ball showed Winsch that she was not yet ready to take the catching duties from Stovroff even if her arm was as good, if not better.

Two days later the Sox played Fort Wayne in an exhibition game in Lafayette, Indiana, on a crisp clear spring day. The Daisies had recently returned from three weeks of spring training in North Carolina. Former major leaguer Jimmy Foxx was the new skipper for the Daisies and he was expected to make the club a contender. "Double XX" had played 20 seasons in the majors and had been enshrined into the National Baseball Hall of Fame in Cooperstown the year before. He had been a great ball player with the Philadelphia Athletics and Boston Red Sox. He slammed out 534 home runs during his career while hitting .325. As great as he was, he had one downfall, his drinking. If he could stay off the sauce, he could be a great manager.

Faut was given the nod to start for the Sox and the Daisies jumped on her for four runs in the first. The Sox– known for making great comebacks–came roaring back in the second with three runs and two more in the third to take the lead, 54. Winsch pulled his wife after five innings to save her arm for the home opener on Saturday. Sue Kidd came in to preserve the Sox win. During the game, first baseman Dottie Mueller severely sprained an index finger fielding a bad throw to her. She would be out a week or two.

The future for the Sox seemed as clear and bright as the deep blue sky after beating the team they thought they would have to fight during the season for the pennant.

Winsch gave the team Wednesday off to rest up for the start of the regular season. He still had plenty of work to do himself. His additional job of general manager, a promotion he received in December, required more paperwork. He was now getting $866.67 a month and his wife was the highest paid player on the team at $541.63 a month.

The manager had chosen this day to decide the fate of a few players to cut before the season began. He decided to send notices to Barb Gates, Peggy Fenton and Lois Sheffield. Other cuts would have to come by June 15 to get down to the 17-player limit.

Winsch could delay losing one player until then because Lib Mahon was still teaching. She had secured a job as a junior high physical fitness teacher at Meesel School in South Bend in the off-season. One of her students was Ruth Davis, one of the two bat girls on the team. Mahon would only play home games until the school year was out.

Players readied their uniforms, washed clothes, shopped or relaxed on the beautiful, partly cloudy spring day with temperatures in the 70s. A few players went to sand dunes of Lake Michigan to soak up some rays. *A Streetcar Named Desire* was playing at the Avon, while Ronald Reagan was starring in *Bedtime for Bonzo* at the new drive-in theater. Players could eat a smorgasbord dinner for $2.95 at Walker's Farm Restaurant in South Bend. A new baseball fiction novel, The *Natural,* had recently been released to bookstores.

Opening Day came on May 15 in Battle Creek, a southern Michigan town about a two-hour jaunt by team bus from South Bend. Most players hated the ride. They enjoyed the company though. Dress was casual and they could smoke on the bus. Many played euchre and poker this day on the way to the first game. Playing helped occupy their minds with something other than the pressure of the first game of the season on the road.

The temperature hovered around a frigid 40 at game time, which kept fans at home watching "What's My Line" on television or listening to "The Shadow" on the radio. A mere crowd of 837 paid admissions filled the stands like the stars in the sky. It was the lowest opening-day crowd in the Belles' history, which began in 1943 in Racine. The franchise moved to Battle Creek in 1951.

Winsch had planned on starting Janet Rumsey on Opening Day, but she was under the weather with a fever and nausea, so he went with veteran pitcher Sue Kidd, who had been 11-7 in 1951. Belles manager Guy Bush, a former Chicago Cubs pitcher nicknamed "The Mississippi Mudcat," countered with Cuban sensation Mickey Perez on the hill. She was one of the Cubans who had been lured to the league after it had held spring training at the tropical island paradise in 1947.

The weather may have been chilly, but the Sox were sizzling this night. They struck for two runs in the second inning thanks to a two-RBI single to left center by Audrey Bleiler. Then Rose Montalbano knocked in Jo Lenard in the sixth for another run. The Sox added three more runs in the seventh inning to take a commanding 6-0 lead, while Sue Kidd shutout the Belles on five hits and five strikeouts.

After the game back in the hotel, catcher Shirley Stovroff put on her chaperone hat and checked to see if everyone was in their room by the 1 a.m. curfew. Stovroff received an extra $159 a month to be the chaperone. She had to make sure players dressed properly at all times and abided by the midnight curfew on the road. At home games, she had little to do.

The next night Rumsey felt much better, so Winsch sent her out to start the game. She had come to the league as an infielder, but Winsch saw potential in her arm during her tryout with the Sox. At five-foot-eight and 135 pounds, she was one of the taller girls on the team and had a lengthy arm to match. Winsch needed more pitching, so he took the prospect. This would be her first game under his microscope.

The attractive rookie hurler was as nervous as an expectant mother in the first inning. She walked the first batter as she struggled to find the plate. The next hitter singled. Then Ruinsey gave up a single to center to score the first run.

After another run scored, Winsch strolled out to the mound to settle her down. "Janet, are you feeling all right?"

"I'm fine. Just nervous, I guess."

"Don't worry. You're trying too hard. Relax and just throw it like you do warming up."

"Okay."

She finally relaxed and retired the side. The Sox came right back in the top of the second to tie the score. Rumsey, still shaky after a rocky first inning, gave up another run in the bottom of the second to put the Belles ahead 3-2. The score remained that way until the top of the seventh. That's when Winsch decided the rookie had thrown enough pitches for one night. He sent in Kidd to pinch hit for her. Kidd came through with a double. Winsch then put the speedier Mary Froning at second to run for Kidd. He had Shorty Pryer lay down a sacrifice bunt to advance Froning to third base. The strategy paid off, because Wagoner came through with a single to score Froning and tie the game. In the eighth inning, the Sox loaded the bases. Winsch called for a squeeze bunt and pitcher Lou Arnold executed perfectly to score the go-ahead run. In the ninth, the Sox scored two insurance runs on two errant throws by the Belles. Winsch was happy with the team's 2-0 start.

The Sox arrived home the next day to a small welcome party on the steps of City Hall and steady showers that cascaded from the gray skies. City Controller Granville Ziegler represented the mayor, who was out of town. The learn was given the key to the city.

The showers continued throughout the day and by game time at 8:15 p.m.., the field at Playland Park was more like the Florida Everglades. The opener with Battle Creek was postponed to Sunday. With another day rest, Faut was more than ready to go after the 100th victory of her career. Only three league pitchers–Connie Wisnewski, Max Kline and Helen Nicol–had accomplished the feat in league history.

The Sox had made a few changes in the off-season to the ballpark, which had been built over a tar-and-cinder two-mile racetrack. More lights were added to remove some of the shadows in the outfield. The six-foot steel-mesh fences were moved in to the league minimum of 210 feet in hopes of more home runs. The league had come up with a livelier 10-inch ball packed with 100 percent wool from DeBeer and Company for the season, so more home runs seemed possible. Manager Winsch had voted against the new ball at the February league meeting, but the other learns had voted in favor of it.

The Sox had hit only four round-trippers the season before, among the lowest in the league. Hardly anyone had hit a ball over the fence at Playland Park. The park was located in a valley next to the St. Joseph River and the ball did not carry well there.

To get more fans in the stands, the team had lowered ticket prices. Bleacher seats in the outfield were cut to 50 cents. The lowest priced grandstand seat was 74 cents. Box seats were $1.50.

After a flag-raising ceremony complete with a high school band, the wives of the mayors of Mishawaka and South Bend threw wildly to each other to signify the first pitch of the opener the next night. The wildness must have affected Faut, who walked the first batter. She allowed a run in the first inning. After that she was untouchable and the Sox rolled to an 11-1 rout.

One of the highlights of the game was a triple steal! Shorty Pryer, who gained the nickname because of her five-foot-one-inch stature, headed the way by sneaking under the pitch to steal home. The swift second baseman also stole second earlier in the inning. Pryer was always a threat to steal any base. In 1951, she led the league in thefts with 129. She also led the league in hits with 133 and runs scored with 106. Her numbers earned her an All-Star squad selection.

No doubt about it, Pryer was a good ball player, but her cocky California style annoyed the manager. They got along like a chemical experiment gone bad. Any time he took her out of a ball game, she would act like a two-year-old child who had been denied candy. He wanted players to put their egos aside. He wanted teamwork. She wanted to play. If they had been married, a divorce would have been in order.

Rain was the victor the next two days at home. Still unhappy with the situation at first base, Dr. Harold Daily wrote Joyce Hill Westerman on May 20 to again offer her a contract. He upped the ante to $110 a month. He could not go any higher because of the pay cap.

When the skies finally cleared, the Sox played un-beaten Grand Rapids for the rights to first place in the league. Winsch wanted this game in the win column, because the two teams had battled for first place all last season.

The Chicks jumped on Sox pitcher Jetty Vincent for three runs in the first thanks to an error by Pryer at short-stop. She booted a sure double-play ball that opened the flood gates and led to three runs scoring. The Chicks added two more runs in the third to take a commanding 5-0 lead.

The Sox chipped away at the lead and were down 5-3 going into the ninth. After the Sox put two runners on base, Faut ended the drama by striking out to end the game.

Winsch placed the blame for the loss on Shorty for her error. But the women made a lot of errors and he had grown somewhat accustomed to them. It still hurt. The only bright spot for the Sox was a homer over the moved-in fence by Stovroff.

The team next traveled to Muskegon for an exhibition double-header. The practice twinbill would give Winsch an opportunity to look at a couple of his not-so-experienced pitchers: Betty Wagoner and Lenora Mandella. Wagoner passed Winsch's test by giving up only three hits in the first game, which the Sox won 3-2. Mandella failed the test in the second game. She held her own until the ninth inning when she gave up three runs and the Sox lost 5-1. Mandella's future on the team was in doubt after the loss. Winsch would have to make cuts soon to get down to the 17-player limit.

That same day the Sox received a letter from Westerman accepting their offer of $110 a week, but she wanted her salary to be tax free. President Bill Sheehan and Dr. Daily discussed the matter over lunch at the Lido and decided to offer her $80 a week salary and $30 tax free from the medical expense fund. This way they could meet the salary cap and partly satisfy her request for tax-free money. Dailey called her back and sold her on the idea. She would arrive after Memorial Day. Daily wrote in his diary:

"Now all we need is a third baseman and this team will be plenty rough."

Rain canceled the first game of the next road series in Battle Creek on May 26. Faut was on the mound for the Sox the next night. She held the Belles to three hits and two runs, yet the Sox could score only two runs, so the score was tied going into the ninth inning. Pryer knocked in the winning run for the Sox before they added three more meaningless runs to win 6-2. Faut was headlined the next day in the South Bend Tribune: "Blue Sox Lead League On Faut's Three-Hitter." The win put the Sox in first place a half game.

The next night the Sox traveled to Fort Wayne for a three-game series. In the first game, the Sox got into a seesaw battle with the Daisies. Going into the fifth, the game was tied. Bleiler stepped to the plate. The tall, skinny pigtailed girl stepped out of the batter's box going after a ball and the umpire called her out. Winsch jumped out of the dugout. He charged up to umpire Ken Valentine and nudged him with his belly as he got into his face. "Why did you call her out?"

"She stepped out of the box."

Winsch looked down at the batter's box, which was obliterated this late in the game. "Where?"

"Right here," Valentine said pointing to the area.

"How can you tell if that's out. The line is gone."

"I don't need a line to tell me where it was."

"I don't believe it. I'm playing this game under protest."

"Okay! Now can we get on with the game?"

The Sox led 4-3 going into the bottom of the ninth. Vincent ran into control problems and gave up two runs to lose the game.

Dr. Dailey and Sheehan had gone to the game and sat with Fort Wayne President Harold Van Orman. After the game, Van Orman turned to them and said, "Well, gentlemen. That is why we are going to win the pennant and you will finish second."

"We may not be in first now, but we will be by the end of the season," Sheehan countered.

"It's a long season," Dailey offered.

"We are in first now and we plan to stay there," Van Orman said.

The loss dropped the Sox from first to third place. Winsch never followed up with a written letter the next day to the protest the game officially. He knew the umpire was right. His complaining was a ploy to upset the umpire in hopes of getting a more favorable call later in the game.

The next night, May 27, was different for the Sox. Unhappy with the loss, Winsch shook up the lineup. He moved Pryer from her leadoff spot and put in Wagoner. The strategy worked, but in reverse. Wagoner failed to get any hits and Pryer went two-for-four. However, this night belonged to Kidd. The pitcher shut down the Daisies on two hits and knocked in the only run needed in the 3-0 win. The win put the Sox back on top of the standings.

The third game of the series featured Faut on the mound. The Sox led 1-0 going into the sixth inning when the Daisies tried to pull off the old hidden-ball trick. With runners on first and second, pitcher Eleanor Moore stepped to the rubber without the ball. Dottie Mueller thought she had the ball and took her lead off second. Second baseman Jean Geissinger walked over to Mueller, pulled the ball out of her glove and tagged her. Instead of calling Mueller out, umpire John Meredith called a balk on Moore. Third baseman Joan Weaver voiced her objections to the call with some choice words. The umpire tossed her. Foxx also argued with Meredith to no avail. The Sox went on to score both runners and win the game, 6-0. The win stretched their league lead to two games over Grand Rapids.

The Sox players were so happy with the win that they sang songs on the bus all the way back to South Bend.

leading the group was Pryer, who had been a singer before she took up professional baseball. They sang some old favorites and "Take Me Out To The Ball Park."

Winsch was delighted his team took two of three games from the Daisies. He also was happy with how the team had started the season. He hoped it could stay in contention through the long, hot summer.

In 1945 the comedy team of Bud Abbott and Lou Costello first performed the routine they called "Who's on First?" Dressed in baseball uniforms, the comedians put on a five-minute show of the craziest named team in baseball. Who was the first baseman, What was on second, I Don't Know was on third and so on.

Winsch faced a who's-on-first-base problem after Joyce Hill Westerman reported to the Sox on June 1. The lefty hit a lofty .242 average and 50 RBI in 1951, 50 she would add some clutch hitting to the lineup. The brown-haired, green-eyed girl was a sure fielder as well.

Winsch was using Dottie Mueller and Pee Wee Wiley at first base. He preferred Mueller over Wiley because she was nearly six feet and made for a larger target for infielders. Wiley, on the other hand, was a much smaller target at five-foot-four. Mueller, a sandy haired woman of German descent with chipped front teeth, also was a pitcher, so she could be used on the mound to give the Sox a total of nine hurlers on the roster. "Sporty," as some players called her, was a veteran of five seasons and had played softball for 10 years before joining the league. Earlier in her career, she pitched a no-hitter for Peoria. She had since lost some zip off her fastball.

Winsch alternated Westerman and Mueller in the double-header against Kalamazoo on May 29. Westerman went hitless in the 3-0 triumph by the Sox in the first game, while Mueller proved her worth with a two-run homer in the nightcap, which the Sox won 6-1. A crowd of 1,339 saw both Sunday games.

On Monday, Sox President Bill Sheehan offered Wimp Baumgartner, Wiley and Lenora Mandella to Kalamazoo for Jane Moffett, a catcher. The lassies were not interested in that deal, so Sheehan offered up Vincent. The Lassies were too concerned with Vincent's high salary of $346.67 a month and passed on the offer.

Sheehan also was still unhappy with the shortstop position and contacted a colored player in Cincinnati who Mueller had sponsored. She was to report on Monday.

Barbara Hoffman went to the team doctor the same day for an exam on her knee, which was giving her pain. Doctor Hoagstead could find nothing wrong with the knee and told Dr. Harold Dailey that he thought Hoffman was taking a holiday.

Also on holiday was Audrey Bleiler, who was having lots of problems in the field because of her pregnant condition. Winsch saw she was not doing well and released her.

The Sox treated their best pitcher, Faut, to a rout the next game with a 13-1 victory at Fort Wayne to give the team a two-game league lead. However, the Daisies came back with a 1-0 shutout the next day in a 12-inning affair.

Going into a doubleheader with Fort Wayne on June 4, the Blue Sox needed to win one of the games to maintain their lead on first place. Keeping the lead wasn't that much of a concern to the players or the manager at the moment. It was too early in the season to worry about that. But there was a matter of pride involved.

The weather cooperated for a change with clear skies and mild temperatures. Winsch answered the question of who would play first base by putting Westerman there, moving Mueller to the bullpen and keeping Wiley on the bench as a reserve player. He liked the pop in Westerman's bat.

Since the ex-Redwing player had arrived, Wiley had spent most of the week on the bench and was saddened by the development. She read over the starting roster after infield practice and took her usual position on the bench. Westerman was on first, again.

Wiley felt a little animosity toward the outsider. Heck, she had been with the team for several years as the bat girl and player and felt it was her time to be in the starting lineup. Pee Wee was born and raised in South Bend and had been a team admirer since she was a little girl. That's when she decided she wanted to be a bat girl some day for the team. After that dream came true, she wanted desperately to play in the league, too. As the bat girl, she had plenty of help and encouragement from the players, who developed her into a fine defensive player. Now she was an attractive young lady with matching brown hair and eyes and the other players looked at her more as competition for a spot on the team than an impressionable bat girl of no threat to their position. She was still a very shy, young girl, though.

Westerman failed to garner any hits in the first game of the doubleheader, but neither did anyone else except for Betty Wagoner. Her single in the third was the only Sox hit of the game. Pitcher Katie Horstman shut down the Sox offense and allowed only an unearned run for a 3-1 victory in the first contest One of the runs came on an error by Shorty Pryer, which irritated the manager.

Winsch decided to put his wife at second base for the second game and let Pryer think about her miscue. It was his way of penalizing her.

When Pryer saw the new lineup card, she became upset She hated sitting on the bench. Plus, she was jealous that she was being replaced by the manager's wife. As

Winsch returned to the dugout from the locker room, Pryer questioned him, "Why am I not in the lineup?"

The manager ignored her. He walked to the other end of the dugout, put his foot up on the bench and spit out a wad of tobacco juice on the dugout floor. It was sort of a response.

Suddenly, all of the emotions inside of Pee Wee spilled out, "Hey! She's asking you a question!"

"Keep out of it!" Winsch replied.

"Roger, dodger," Pee Wee said sarcastically, turned and walked away.

"Pee Wee! Hit the showers! And don't come back until you're told."

A funeral-home silence descended over the dugout. An angry Winsch spit out some tobacco and kicked a ball across the dugout floor. Then he went out on the field to meet with the umpires to exchange line-up cards.

Pee Wee picked up her gear and glanced at Shorty as she left. She took a shower as ordered then hung around in the stands to watch the rest of the game and talk with Winsch afterwards.

The floodgates opened for the Sox in the second game as they scored five runs in the first three innings. But Fort Wayne answered with five of their own and the score was tied 5-5 going into the eighth inning. A tired Lou Arnold gave up a couple of hits and two errors by Faut at second led to four more runs by the Daisies, In the ninth down 9-5, Winsch brought in Belly Wagoner from right field to pitch. He shifted his wife to right and brought in Pryer to play second base. Pryer was cold coming off the bench and booted two balls, allowing the Daisies to score another run. That gave the Sox a total of 10 errors in the game!

The Blue Sox rallied for three runs in the bottom of the ninth, but could get no closer than the tying run at the plate. The double-header loss dropped them to a game behind the Daisies. Wiley never did get a chance to talk to the angry manager. She went home to wait for word from him.

The next night Wagoner limited the Daisies to two runs, while the Sox scored four. The two teams were deadlocked for first. Wiley sat at home wondering her fate and when she would get called back. The Sox left on a road trip to Kalamazoo the next morning, a Friday, minus Pee Wee. She stayed at home with her parents.

Wiley finally received an answer on Monday. She got her answer when the postman arrived around noon. He came with a letter from the team. She opened it and could hardly believe her eyes. It read: "This is to notify those concerned, that Janet Wiley is being given a thirty (30) day suspension, effective June 5, 1952. REASON: Conduct unbecoming on the field. SUSPENSION REQUESTED BY: Team Manager, Karl Winsch. Signed: W.F. Sheehan, Pres."

Tears came to Wiley's eyes as she read the letter.

"What's wrong?" questioned her mother.

"The team has suspended me for a month!"

"Oh, my God! That's ridiculous!"

"I'm never going to go back there again!"

Pee Wee thought her playing days were over and just the thought of that sent ripples of emotions through her body and a flood of tears to her eyes. Players were taught not to cry on the playing field, so they held their emotions until later. The letter served as the release to all her pent-up feelings. She sobbed like a baby in her mother's arms. It was like she had lost a loved one. Baseball had been her first love. She had put everything else in her life to the side to concentrate on the game. Now the game was gone.

"I'll talk with Chet Grant. He can talk to the league," her mother assured her. Grant was a former manager of the

Sox when Pee Wee had been a bat girl with the team.

"Well, I'm not going to help out with their fan club anymore," said her father, Adam Wiley. The tailor was named vice president of the team's fan club in March.

The colored woman from Cincinnati never showed up on Monday, so the team was still short a decent shortstop.

Two days later, the Sox asked for waivers on Wiley, so they could release her. No teams claimed her though, so she was still Sox property. Because she was suspended, the Sox did not pay her and could afford to get a replacement. The salary cap had been raised to $5,700 in late May, so the Sox had some extra funds to play with.

The deadline for the player and salary limit was quickly approaching on June 15, a Sunday. The Sox sent Rose Montalbano to Battle Creek for cash. With Pryer at second and Gerty Dunn at short, the little Italian infielder was no longer needed.

On June 13 the league held their regular monthly meeting. Battle Creek President Charles Tidley again brought up the Sue Kidd for Pat Crawley trade. He claimed that South Bend's offer was not valid and that Kidd should go to the Belles.

"We offered Crawley $300 a month to play. What did South Bend offer her?" Tidley asked.

"We sent her a contract for $260 a month, which is what she said that you offered her. She wasn't interested because she was a stewardess for United," Sheehan replied.

"You didn't offer her enough money. That's why she won't come back!"

"Money wasn't the issue. She wanted job security."

"You acted improperly! We should get Kidd!"

"Get out of here!"

"Gentlemen!" Board President Harold Van Orman shouted to break up the argument. "I want to table this discussion until later."

Battle Creek was in dire need of a pitcher, so Van Orman talked Fort Wayne into letting Mirtha Marrero go to the Belles for the trade minimum of $100. He then talked Sheehan into paying the $100 for the trade as a compromise to Battle Creek. The deal satisfied Tidley and the controversy was finally over.

Meanwhile, the Sox went on a three-game winning streak on the road to get back to a first-place tie with Fort Wayne. After a 6-3 loss to Grand Rapids, the Sox again went on a win skeen, pulling off nine victories in a row and talking a 4 1/2-game lead over Fort Wayne in the process. The winning streak included two victories by Faut, one of which was a seven-inning one-hitter, to send her record to 5-0 on the season. The ace hurler walked three and fanned four on her way to a one-hit victory over Battle Creek.

Also during the win streak, Jetty Vincent added another name as she tied the knot with Robert William Mooney on June 14. The attractive woman of French descent (her mother's name was DuFrense) with dark brown hair and hazel eyes was marrying an Air Force man. Only a few players came to the small ceremony at St. Patrick's Church in South Bend. Wagoner was maid of honor and one of Jetty's brothers was the best man.

Winsch took advantage of bride's emotional high by starting her in the first game of the doubleheader with Rockford that evening. She held the Peaches to four hits and a run, while the Sox tallied 11 runs.

Two days later Sheehan tried to deal Lou Arnold and Wiley to Kalamazoo for Jane Moffett. Kalamazoo manager Bill Allington was trying to get Wiley for free and had invited her up to the club. She drove to Kalamazoo, but became homesick on the way there and returned to South Bend.

Unaware that Battle Creek had tried to get her back, Kidd faced the Belles and lost 3-1 to end the winning streak. In the game, Pryer banged up her ankle sliding into second base. Her slide was too late and her right foot turned severely in the process. She was expected to be out of action for a week or two. To replace her, the Sox received Marge Wenzell on loan from Battle Creek. Before Wenzell arrived, Barb Hoffman played at second base for a game.

On June 23, the Blue Sox were in Rockford to face the Peaches. Winsch put Janet Rumsey on the mound. Rumsey was a homegrown girl. She was born and raised in Moores Hill, Indiana. Her father got her interested in baseball. Because her school didn't have a softball team, she played on the boy's team in junior high school. When she was 18, she saw a movie short on the Fort Wayne Daisies at the local theater and wrote the team. She was invited to a tryout by the team, but she didn't make the grade. Then in 1951, she tried out for the Sox and Winsch saw more potential in her arm than in her bat and turned her into a pitcher rather than a fielder. The tall, lean pitcher with dark hair struggled to a 4-8 season in 1951, but Winsch saw hope in her arm and continued to work with the hurler. He figured some day that she would turn into a good pitcher and hoped this would be the season. He tried to show some confidence in her by putting her in the regular rotation.

In the bottom of the first inning, Rumsey pitched herself into a jam: two outs and runners on the corners. She saw the runner on first break to second out of the corner of her eye. She made a forward motion, stopped, whirled around and threw the ball into centerfield. Umpire Ken Valentine called a balk and allowed both runners to advance, which scored a run.

Winsch felt the call was wrong and leaped out of the dugout like lion going after its prey. He came up to Valentine and belly bumped him. "Why the balk?"

"Because she started her windup and didn't hesitate long enough to back *off* the rubber."

Winsch smelled alcohol on Valentine's breath. He could see that the umpires eyes were glassy. "She never started her windup!"

"Oh, yes, she did."

"What's the rule book say?"

"Get out of here!"

Some Sox players came out of the dugout and swarmed around the short umpire like killer bees. They talked in gibberish, so he could not understand them.

"Youiz stuizpidiz!"

"Assizholeiz!"

"Homizeriz!"

"Are you going to throw me out of the game for this?"

"Damn you! Get out of here!" Valentine barked back. His face turned red and he clinched his fists. All the players around him made him feel claustrophobic.

Winsch bumped him again. "Put me out!"

Valentine swung at Winsch but missed. A second swing caught Winsch's chin. The Sox players grabbed the beserk umpire. Valentine caught Faut with a punch. Then he grabbed Jo Lenard around the neck.

Wimp Baumgarter wrapped her arms around Winsch to get him out of the fracas. The manager tried to break the grip, but the strong catcher held on like a cowboy roping a calf at a rodeo.

Two police officers in the stands rushed onto the field to break up the riot. They were joined by others, including base umpire Casey Koweleski, Peaches President Clarence Pierce and manager Bill Allington.

The peacemakers finally broke up the riot. Winsch and Valentine were escorted off the field by the police. Winsch angrily protested the game to Koweleski on his way off the field. Then he told Pierce that Valentine had been drinking. The umpire waited at the gate for Winsch, but the policemen made sure no more fighting would occur and sent Valentine on his way.

Winsch went back to the hotel, showered and changed into a plaid shirt and black pants. He returned to the park to see the outcome of the game. The manager sat in deep left field so as not to be noticed. But an usher spotted him and reported him to the police. When Winsch saw them coming for him, he got up and left the park again. On his way out of the stadium, the gatekeeper told him that Valentine was looking for him. Winsch could hardly believe the umpire had any fight left in him.

The two runs that Rockford scored in the first as a result of the balk turned out to be the difference in the game as the Peaches won 4-3.

When word of the incident reached the league office the next day, league business manager Earl McCammon immediately suspended Winsch indefinitely and fined everyone involved. He also banished Valentine from the league for life for his pre-game drinking. He sent a telegram to the Sox with the news.

The South Bend Board of Directors called an emergency meeting to hear more about what had occurred on the field. Winsch told them what had happened that night and how he was stalked afterwards by the umpire. An article in the Rockford newspaper went along with what Winsch had told them. The Board asked the manager to write a letter to McCammon and give his side of the story.

Lib Mahon was named as the interim manager. Mahon was not the first woman manager in the league. Others had filled in temporarily before. The only player ever hired as the manager of an All-American team was Bonnie Baker, who took over the Kalamazoo Lassies midway through the 1950 season. Under her direction, the club moved from last place to a playoff spot During the 1951 season, Ernestine Petras took over the Kenosha Comets for a few weeks in an emergency.

Mahon was named as manager because of her experience and maturity. She started playing in 1944 and joined South Bend in 1945, 50 she had more time on the team than any other player. She was a school teacher, too, which showed she could direct people. She also had been an All-Star twice. Players respected her.

Mahon benched herself and put Wagoner in right field so she could concentrate on managing duties in her first game as manager. Ace pitcher Jean Faut was on the mound and shut down Battle Creek. The Sox players made Mahon's job easy as they scored eight runs to the Belles solo run.

During the contest, McCammon arrived at South Bend to hear Winsch's side of the story first hand, because he had heard something different from the Battle Creek officials. After Winsch explained his story, the business manager changed the suspension to three games. He let the $25 fine stand, however.

After the game ended, McCammon spoke to the players involved in the incident to get a clearer picture of what had occurred and to give them a chance to defend themselves against the fines he had levied. McCammon changed his mind about fining the players.

The next evening, Sue Kidd got revenge on an earlier loss to Battle Creek on Ladies Night, which brought 1,200 fans to Playland Park. All women were admitted on payment of a 10-cent tax ticket. Kidd gave up just two runs, while the Sox scored seven.

Going into a three-game series with Fort Wayne, Winsch was back and the Sox led the Daisies by three games. If the Sox were to lose all three games, then the two teams would be tied for first on July 1. The team in first on

July 1 would face the All-Star Team on July 7 at that team's park.

The All-Star game format was quite different in 1943, the first year of the league. All-Star players from Racine and Kenosha faced the All-Stars from Rockford and South Bend. The teams played a twi-night doubleheader at Wrigley Field, which was the first night game ever held at the Chicago Cub's home park. Portable light stands were used for the game. The game was suspended in 1944 and 1945 due to the war and resumed in 1946.

The Sox dropped the first two games of the series, 8-2 and 6-5. For the third game, he named his undefeated wife for the must-win game for the right to face the All-Star Team.

Fort Wayne touched Faut for an unearned run in the first inning. After that Faut's pitches were invisible. In the bottom of the fifth inning, the Sox scored four runs on hits by Faut, Shirley Stovroff and Marge Wenzell. The Sox won 5-1 and would host the All-Star Game in a week. After the game, some of the older players went to the nearby Boat Club to celebrate. They smoked, danced, drank beer and played the slot machines. Curfew was not enforced for home games, so they stayed out late that night.

Sox players chosen for the All-Star Team were Shorty Pryer; top vote getter at second base; Faut, second best pitcher; Stovroff, top catcher; and Betty Wagoner, second among outfielders. How-ever, because South Bend won the honor to play the All-Stars, the four Sox players would play for their own team and they would be replaced by other players on the All-Star Team. The selections were made by the press in the six team cities.

The Sox stretched their home winning streak to 14 games until Kalamazoo's Doris Sams stroked a grand slam to beat the Sox 94 on July 1. The loss came on the heals of a one-hit shutout by Rumsey in the first game of a doubleheader. It was the best game Rumsey had ever pitched and Winsch thought she was coming of age.

The league held a meeting in South Bend on July 5 to decide on the Wiley suspension and hear about the Winsch suspension. Chet Grant came to the meeting to appeal the Wiley suspension and ask for her release.

Winsch spoke first. "I suspended her for conduct unbecoming on the field. I was talking to another player when she rudely interrupted us and talked out of line. She repeatedly talked back to me before I sent her to the showers. Then she came back in the stands and continued to criticize me and the Sox management during the game. I decided to suspend her for a month."

Grant's story was quite different. "That's not exactly how it happened. Miss Wiley assured me she did not say anything derogatory to Mr. Winsch. She was simply asking him to listen to a player who wanted an explanation of why she had been left out of a game. He wouldn't give her an explanation and that is when she spoke up in her behalf. She feels the 30-day suspension was much too severe. You have penalized her by not paying her and jeopardizing her playing career. She thinks she should get back pay for the suspension and an unconditional release from her contract."

The Board suspended the meeting until after the game was over. When they returned they finished discussing suspension. A motion was made to give Wiley an outright release and 20 days back pay. The motion was not seconded, so another motion was made to give her a release. It was seconded and passed. Wiley would get her release. She was now a free agent and could sign with any team.

Going into the All-Star game, the Sox were 3~ 15 and led Fort Wayne by four-and-a-half games after sweeping the Daisies three games in a row in Fort Wayne. Faut gained her tenth victory of the season without any defeats in an 11th inning 2-1 victory over the Daisies.

The All-Star Team was managed by Rockford skipper Bill Allington, a hard-nosed veteran who had managed women's softball teams before he began managing in the league. The starting lineup included Maxine Kline, Rockford, pitcher; Ruth Richard, Rockford, catcher; Betty Foss, Fort Wayne, first base; Joan Berger, Rockford, second base; Dorothy Schroeder, Fort Wayne, shortstop; Fern Shollenberger; Kalamazoo, third base; Eleanor Callow, Rockford, left field; Doris Sams, Kalamazoo, left field; Doris Sams, Kalamazoo, center field; and Jo Weaver, right field. Others selected for the team were Rose Gacioch, Rockford, pitcher; Gloria Cordes, Kalamazoo, pitcher; Jean Cione, Battle Creek, pitcher; Dorothy Doyle, Rockford, utility infielder; Alice Deschaine, Rockford, utility infielder; Sadie Satterfield, Grand Rapids, utility outfielder; Connie Wisniewski, Grand Rapids, utility outfielder; Rita Briggs, Battle Creek, backup catcher; and Alma Ziegler; Battle Creek, second base.

A forecast of rain during the day kept the game from being a sellout. A cloudy sky greeted the players at South Bend.

The Sox were considered the "best balanced clutch team" in the league, according to a South Bend Tribune reporter. The reporter thought Winsch would have his wife start the game, but the Sox manager chose to save his wife for a game which counted in the standings. Instead, he named Betty Wagoner to pitch.

She did a fine job until the sixth inning. Then all hell broke loose. The all-stars had figured out Wagoner's sidearm delivery by then and scored six runs by the time the inning came to an end. Wagoner was replaced on the mound by Jetty Vincent Mooney.

Foss grounded a Mooney delivery to third base and was called out at first base on a close play. She argued with the umpire over the call and he tossed her out of the game. She retaliated by taking his hat off and stomping on it. The Sox tied the score in the bottom of the eighth before the All-Stars scored one in the ninth to win the game, 7-6. Allington was able to get all his players into the game, much like managers of Major league All-Star games. Winsch put a dozen players into his lineup. The game drew 3,528 fans, much more than the Sox usually drew.

Winsch's strategy not to pitch his wife in the All-Star Game backfired. The extra rest did no good when she returned to the mound on July 9 versus Kalamazoo. Doris Sams, who hit a two-run homer in the All-Star Game, knocked in the winning run in the sixth off Faut. The loss was Faut's first of the year. The loss also was the second loss of the night to the lassies. It began a slide from the five-game cushion the Sox had over Fort Wayne after the All-Star break. The Sox lost the next game to Kalamazoo, too.

Then the South Bend team went on a road trip to Grand Rapids, where they were swept and their lead dropped to two-and-a-half games. To make matters worse, Faut was hurt in Grand Rapids. She was struck on the wrist playing third base and the joint swelled up like a balloon. She returned home for x-rays, while the team went to Rockford for a four-game series. The x-rays proved negative, but she would be out until the wrist was better.

Because regular third baseman Barbara Hoffman was already out with a knee injury suffered in Kalamazoo the week before, Winsch was forced to put pitcher Mooney at third. Pryer was now recovered from an ankle injury, but Winsch was using Wenzell at second.

Another doubleheader disaster to Rockford left the Sox with a half-game league lead. South Bend had lost eight of their last 10 games. Most games had been on the road and the Sox were returning to the friendly confines of

Playland Park for a couple of series.

After yet another rainout, the Sox faced the Chicks. Kidd and Rumsey pitched the team to two victories to give the team some breathing room at the top.

Faut was healed enough to return to the lineup—not to pitch, but to play third. The Sox celebrated the return with a win over Grand Rapids. The game featured Chick player Inez Voyce punching an umpire. The incident occurred after a called third strike by umpire Al Stover. When she grabbed his arm, he ejected her from the game. That's when she took a swing at him and connected a glancing blow off his head. The Chicks bench later erupted with profanities when the Sox came to bat, so Stover excused them as well, which left only the players on the field to finish the rest of the game. The league later fined Voyce $10 and suspended her for 10 days.

The Sox had a chance to sweep the Chicks without Voyce in the lineup, but the other players picked up the slack and whipped the Sox, 7-2.

After another rainout, the Sox hosted Rockford for a doubleheader and a single game. After cruising to a 9-0 win in the opener, the Sox lost the second game of the doubleheader, 2-1. A 4-3 loss the next day prompted Winsch to order batting practice after the game. He was disgusted with the team's performance. The team's lead was down to a half game over Fort Wayne. Winsch was tired of looking in the rearview mirror and seeing the Daisies.

Extra innings are suppose to rid baseball of the tie game.

Tie games were not suspended and finished later in the All-American league like in the Major leagues. They simply did not count in the standings.

The July 25th contest at Battle Creek was delayed until 10 p.m. because of an earlier contest on the field between two Army teams. The league had a curfew of

11:30 p.m. so if the game ended in a tie it was all for
naught. Winsch and Battle Creek manager Guy Bush
agreed to play nine innings regardless of the rule. They also
agreed not to play extra innings if the game was tied after
nine innings.

When 11:30p.m. came about, South Bend led 3-1
after seven innings. Had the managers gone by league rules,
the Sox would have won. But two more innings had to be
played according to their own agreement. With two out in
the bottom of the ninth, Shorty Pryer muffed an easy
grounder to let the tying run score, which is how the game
ended. The game would go down as a tie and not go in the
standings. The tie resulted in the Daisies catching up to the
Sox.

On July 28, Pee Wee Wiley received and acknowledged a letter from Bill Sheehan, president of the South
Bend Blue Sox. The letter terminated her contract with the
team effective July 5. Now she was a free agent and could
sign with any team she wished. As late as it was in the
season, she figured her year was over and she was satisfied
to make a comeback next year with another team.

The Sox went on a three-game winning streak at
Grand Rapids. In one of the games, Faut returned to the
mound for her 11th win. Pryer also redeemed her error in
the tie game when she scored the winning run in another
game after stealing second and third base. The short winning streak gave the Sox a two-game lead, but a loss in the
last game of the Chicks' series narrowed the margin to one
game.

Two games later Pryer got on Winsch's bad side when
she failed to cover first base on a bunt and a run scored in
the mix up. Winsch threw his hat to the ground in disgust.
Pryer made up for the mental error later with an RBI,
which helped the Sox win.

The second baseman went hitless in three at bats the

next game. This led Winsch to yank her from the lineup in a double swap when he changed pitchers. The move upset Pryer. The Sox still lost 3-2 to Kalamazoo.

Pryer was back in the lineup the next game, which the Sox won. A doubleheader win followed which took the Blue Sox to a record of 30-11 at home and 19-17 on the road. They maintained a two-game lead in the standings, too. A day later, Pryer helped the team take another double-header by going three-for-five with a triple, two runs scored and a stolen base.

On August 5, South Bend traveled to Fort Wayne for a four-game series. While a little early to be a critical series between the front-running teams, it was an important series just the same. Winsch would be satisfied with a split.

Before the game, a gas truck poured some fuel on the field in an effort to dry it. The strong smell was nauseating to some players. After the field was lit, a flame trailed the truck as it pulled away from the field, which provided some tense moments for the players. The flame stopped short of the truck. The dangerous technique did the trick and the game would be played with a drier infield.

Sue Kidd's start on the mound was about as ominous as the cumulus clouds that threatened to prevent the game. Winsch employed a shift strategy whenever Betty Foss came to bat. He would move all his fielders to the right side, except for third baseman Barb Hoffman, who he moved to shortstop.

But the big threat came not from Foss this night. A triple by Dottie Schroeder ignited a three-run downpour on the Sox. Doubles by Gertie Dunn and Betty Wagoner helped the Sox bounce right back in the second to take a 4-3 lead. Kidd improved from there on out and the Sox squeaked out a 5-4 win.

After the game back in the hotel, some of the players got together in Hoffman's room. They talked about the game. Then the discussion turned to who was the best outfielder on the team and it turned into a shouting match. Chaperone Shirley Stovroff heard the disturbance and told the girls to quiet down.

Faut took the mound the next night to try and assure her husband of his minimum wish of a split. She had a 4-3 lead going into the bottom of the ninth inning when the team stated playing like Little Leaguers. Two errors and a bad throw led the Sox to losing.

When the Daisies won the third game with a 5-2 score, the Sox needed to win the last game to stay in front of the Daisies in the standings. Pitcher Jetty Vincent Mooney was as shaky as a drunk and gave up five runs early. Winsch saw she was too wild and replaced her with Betty Wagoner. Then the team acted liked they had the year before. They rallied for 16 hits and eight runs over the next four innings to take a 9-5 lead. Wagoner held on to win 9-7 and give the Sox the split of the series.

The road trip continued to third-place Rockford. Pryer fumbled an easy grounder, which led to two runs scoring and a 2-1 loss.

Faut and Rumsey threw back-to-back five hitters the next two games to give the Sox the edge in the three-game set. It also gave them a game advantage in the standings over Fort Wayne, which had come to Playland Park for three games.

Kidd was shaky in the beginning of the first contest and allowed four runs in the first two innings. The Daisies pitchers started a walkathon. Nineteen walks later the Sox strolled to a 17-4 victory.

The second game promised a lower score as Faut and Maxine Kline were pitching. However; neither was very sharp at the onset as Faut gave up four runs in the first and Kline allowed three runs. The Sox surged to a 7-4 lead to send Kline to the pine. Faut hung on for her sixteenth victory of the season.

The last game of the series lasted a little more than an inning before being rained out. Meanwhile, the league announced it had taken over the running of Battle Creek Belles because the team's financial backers had withdrawn their support. The Belles scheduled the next game against the Sox at a park formerly used by the Toledo Mudhens. The future of the franchise past the season was left in doubt.

Rockford came to South Bend for a four-game series and surprised the Sox by winning the first two games. Fortunately, Faut pitched the third game of the series and broke the up the losing streak. In the last game of the series, the Sox led early. Then things went awry. With Rockford runners on second and third, Gertie Dunn collided with a Rockford runner going for a pop up. The ball dropped in for a hit.

Winsch charged out of the dugout and ran up to umpire Al Stover. "That's runner interference! The runner should be out!"

"I didn't see any interference on the play," said Stover.

"The Rockford runner got in the way of my fielder" Winsch pleaded.

"I don't think so."

"Maybe the other umpire saw it."

The umpires conferred, but the decision stood. The bad call opened up the flood gates and by the time the inning ended, the Sox were down 5-2. Winsch changed pitchers but the bleeding continued. The Sox lost 13-3.

The Sox traveled to Toledo to face Battle Creek for one game. The game was held up for 20 minutes when a surprising amount of fans, some 4,000, showed up and there were still long lines at the ticket counter at game time.

The Sox won the coin toss and became the home team on the neutral field. Janet Rumsey was assigned to pitch in the never-before-seen ballpark. She must have felt out of sorts on the strange mound for she gave up three runs in the second inning. The Sox never made up the difference and lost 3-2, which left them with a half-game lead over Fort Wayne.

The next day the Sox traveled to Grand Rapids for a three-game series. South Bend was shutout, 8-0, in the first contest. The Sox were shutout again the next game, 6-0, but Faut salvaged the second game of the doubleheader by reversing the roles on the Chicks with her own shutout.

Meanwhile, Fort Wayne was winning and tied South Bend in the standings. The Sox ship was beginning to take on water.

Now that South Bend and Fort Wayne were dead-locked in first with identical records, the race for the pennant was becoming a real pressure cooker. Manager Winsch's patience with the team was wearing thin. He'd do just about anything for a win. He had a deep desire to win the pennant and the championship for the second year in a row.

At Grand Rapids on a fair and pleasant Saturday evening, August 23, Winsch made some maneuvers like the generals in Korea, where another battle was going on. At a crucial point late in the game with the Blue Sox ahead 3-2, the field general began his strategy. With two outs and a player on first base, he decided to pinch hit for Sue Kidd, who was showing signs of tiring.

"Lib, pinch hit for Kidd," he said to his veteran player.

Just as Mahon was about to step into the batter's box, Winsch changed his mind. He thought Joyce Westerman would be better used in this spot than Mahon, because she was a left-handed batter and the pitcher was a righty. The odds of Westerman getting a hit were better than the right-handed hitting Mahon.

He turned to Westerman. "Joyce, go in and hit for Mahon." Winsch called time out while the exchange was made.

Westerman was a little surprised by the maneuver. Mahon understood what he was doing, but he should of thought of it before now.

Before Westerman stepped in, she looked at Winsch for the signals. He flashed the steal sign to the runner on first, Gertie Dunn, and a take sign to Westerman.

The first pitch was a high fastball that made for an easy throw to second by catcher Mary Rountree. Dunn was easily gunned down and the inning was over. Winsch had wasted two batters. He could have stayed with Kidd.

Janet Rumsey had a chance to save the game in the ninth inning, but she gave up a home run to Inez Voyce, her second round tripper of the game. When Rumsey came to bat in the 10th inning, Winsch sent Westerman in to hit for her. Before he did, he talked to the umpire.

"I'm pulling in Westerman to pinch hit. She never did get a chance to bat before," he told the umpire.

"Okay," umpire John Bloke agreed without thinking.

After Westerman walked, Manager Bill English ran out to confront Bloke. "You can't allow her to come back in the game," he complained.

"Why not?" the umpire said.

"Because she was announced. That counts as a time at bat."

"Just a sec. Let me check with the scorekeeper."

The confused umpire turned to the scorekeeper for help. The scorekeeper looked at his book and confirmed that Westerman had enterted the game in the ninth.

"Batter's out!" Bloke yelled.

Winsch jogged to the pair behind home plate. "Why is she out?"

"Because she entered the game in the ninth inning. You can't put her back in again." `

"Are you sure?"

"Quite sure."

"Okay. Sorry."

Winsch knew what he did was wrong. His maneuver had backfired, but he still wanted an appropriate explanation.

In the 11th inning, Voyce was a nemesis again as she stroked her fourth hit of the game and advanced to second after a walk with one out. The Blue Sox tried to convert a double play to end the inning, but Shorty Pryer's throw from second got away from Dottie Mueller and Voyce scored the winning run.

Fortunately for the Sox, Fort Wayne lost to third-place Rockford, who was eight games back and almost out of the race entirely.

The Sox fell from grace the next night when they lost at Grand Rapids under a dense canopy of stars. They blew an early lead again and lost by a run, 5-4. Voyce victimized the Sox again with a home run to knot the score. Then veteran all-star Connie Wisniewski singled, stole second, advanced to third on a single and scored the winning run on a sacrifice. The Blue Sox seemed to be falling apart under the pressure of the pennant race. Fort Wayne beat Rockford to take over first place by a game.

To get more fans in the stands, the Blue Sox management promoted the next game at home against Battle Creek as "Back to School Day." All youngsters under age 13 would be admitted free to the game. Of course parents would have to bring their children to the ball park, so the

team was really after their money. It had been warm during
the day in the 80s, but by game time at 8:15 p.m., the
temperature was about 70 degrees and a crescent moon
rode the sky.
    Jetty Vincent Mooney gave up two runs in the first
inning to the Belles. Battle Creek added another pair of
runs in the third. In the bottom of the sixth inning, Mooney
came up to bat with the bases loaded. She ripped a liner to
center that went through the legs of Ruth Middleton and
rolled all the way to the fence. All three runners scored and
Mooney cruised into third base. Pryer singled to score
Mooney and tie the game. Both teams blew opportunities to
finish the game in the ninth inning, so the game became an
extra-inning affair. In the bottom of the 11th inning, Betty
Wagoner was given a free pass to first. She stole second
and advanced to third on a wild pitch. Then Stoll singled to
left to bring in the winning run.
    Despite the victory, the Sox fell another half-game
behind the Daisies, who swept a doubleheader from
Kalamazoo. The Daisies were as hot as the weather, which
was typical during the dog days of summer in northern
Indiana and southern Michigan.
    The Sox next traveled to Kalamazoo for a four-game
senes. Winsch selected his wife to pitch the first game
against the laassies. Her record was 18-2 and her control
was never better. She had shutout Grand Rapids in her last
appearance although she had given up seven hits. Shorty
beat out an infield hit to lead off the game. She scored on
Betty Wagoner's double to the gap in left center. Shorty
also dropped a daring squeeze bunt on a two-strike count in
the sixth to bring home Mueller for the third run of the
game. Faut breezed through the Lassies and allowed only
three singles on the night to pitch her second consecutive
shutout. Home plate umpire John Santa called only 16 of
Faut's pitches balls all night, which was thought to be a

league record; however, the league hadn't kept accurate individual pitching records in years, so nobody knew for sure.

Meanwhile, Fort Wayne whipped Grand Rapids, 8-3, to stay one-and-a-half games up in the standings. The next night the Sox jumped out to a 2-0 lead early and by the bottom of the ninth inning the Sox had extended the lead to 5-2. The win seemed assured. Then pitcher Sue Kidd allowed a run to score. To make matters worse, she put two more on base, which put the winning run at the plate with two outs. Winsch thought Kidd had enough left to get one more out. How wrong he was. Jean lovell put a Kidd offering over the left-field fence to win the game for Kalamazoo.

The defeat took the air out of Winsch and the Sox players. The team usually came from behind themselves to win games. Now it seemed the situation was reversed. It was disheartening. Team morale was at its lowest point of the season and it needed to be at its highest for the team to win another pennant.

Luckily for the Sox, Fort Wayne was beat 8-4 by Grand Rapids. The Sox remained a game and a half back. Thursday was fireworks night in the Michigan city and a large crowd was on hand for the festivities after the game. Game fireworks began right away as the Sox exploded for two runs in the top of the first on a two-run double by Faut. The Lassies countered with a larger rally in the bottom of the stanza and scored five runs off Janet Rumsey. The Sox managed to tie the game in the sixth inning only to give up three more runs in the bottom of the sixth to let the game slip away. The Lassies won 9-5.

At the same time the Sox were losing, the Daisies were winning. They beat the Chicks and extended their lead to two-and-a-half games over the Sox. With six games left in the season, the Sox needed wins.

In the last game of a series on the road in
Kalamazoo, Winsch decided to shake up the line up and put
Marge Wenzell at second base in place of Shorty Pryer,
because she had gone hitless the night before. She didn't
think she should ride the bench, considering she was an
All-Star and the best base stealer in the league. Pryer was a
tough player because of her background. She had served in
the Marine Corps prior to joining the league. After the war
was over, the "buck" sergeant became a nightclub singer in
Reno, Nevada. She grew tired of the nightclub scene and
switched to a baseball career like her father tried to do. He
missed making it to the big leagues when he suffered a
broken elbow in spring training with the Chicago White
Sox. She wanted to make him proud of her by making it in
the All-American league and becoming a star player.
Winsch was standing in her way. She was no longer happy
playing for him. She wanted to be traded.

The game was scoreless until the sixth inning. By
then the night sky glared white from the stadium lights.
Clouds prevented any stars from showing through.
Kalamazoo scored on an errant throw by Mueller to first
base. Going into the top of the ninth inning, the Lassies
were still ahead 1-0. With two out in the ninth inning Betty
Wagoner reached first base on a single, only the second hit
off of Gloria Cordes.

Winsch turned to the dugout and yelled from the
third-base coaches box, "Shorty! Go in and run for Wagoner!"

"Maluchi! I'm not ready! I've got to put my spikes
on."

Pryer had already taken off her spikes and changed
into her street shoes in anticipation of the game's end.

Winsch became furious. His face turned red as
Georgia clay and he shook his head from side to side in
disgust.

As Pryer tied her spikes, she said to others on the bench, "Why is he putting me in to run for her when she's as fast as I am? She's warm and I'm cold."

Nobody answered.

When Pryer was ready, she jogged out to first. Winsch went through his signals: right-index finger on his nose, left-hand pat on top of his hat, right-hand rub across his chest, left-hand pull on the ear lobe, right-hand brush of the pants and left hand wipe of the forehead. He had given her the steal signal on the first pitch. He also had given the batter the take sign.

Lassies manager Mitch Skupien figured Pryer might be running on the first pitch, so he called for a pitch out. When Cordes let go of the pitch, catcher Jenny Romatowski saw Pryer take off out of the comer of her eye. She stood up and threw as hard as she could to second. The throw was perfect. Pryer was out.

The game was over.

South Bend dropped to three-and-a-half games behind Fort Wayne, almost putting them mathematically out of the running for the pennant. The Daisies had four games left, the Sox had five.

After the game ended, Sox director Dr. Harold Daily pulled Winsch aside. "What was the delay all about in the ninth inning?"

"Shorty had to put her spikes on."

"I want her suspended for a week."

"That's fine with me. We're out of the race now no thanks to her."

"Tell her now and we will send her a letter tomorrow."

"You got it."

The suspension would put Pryer out of the lineup until the playoffs began. A suspension was a stiff penalty, because other teams usually fined players for not being ready to play.

Winsch pulled Fryer off the bus to inform her of the suspension. "I'm suspending you for a week."

"Why?"

"For not being ready to play."

"That's ridiculous."

"You need to be ready to play at all times."

"I'm sorry, it won't happen again."

"You can play when we get to the playoffs."

"Yeah, right."

A dejected Pryer returned to her seat. She told her roommate, Shirley Stovroff, and Lib Mahon of the suspension. Both women decided that if Shorty was going to be suspended for a week then they would not play either.

Mahon had already decided she was going to quit the team at the end of the season to take up teaching full time. So she figured she had nothing to lose by talking to the feisty manager.

On the bus ride home, the tall, dark-haired woman approached Winsch about the suspension.

"Hey, Karl. Shorty is sorry she wasn't ready when you called upon her, but she thought she wasn't going to play again," Mahon explained.

"Apology accepted, but the suspension stands."

"But we need her. We can still catch Fort Wayne before the season ends."

"We don't need her. She is one player. This is a team *effort*. She hasn't shown that she's a team player."

"Yeah, but—"

"No buts! She's been leading up to this for all season. Now she'll have to pay the price," Winsch said angrily.

Mahon reacted with some of her own fire. "If the suspension stands then other players - including myself - will leave the team."

"Fine. If that's your decision. The suspension stands. No ifs, ands or buts."

"You asked for it," Mahon turned and returned to her seat.

The next day Shorty protested her suspension in writing to Sox President Bill Sheehan and league President Harold Van Orman. Van Orman had been told that Shorty had quit the team.

When he asked her about that by phone, she vehemently denied it: "Winsch suspended me. I positively did not quit."

Before the next game began, Mahon and Stovroff held a meeting in the locker room to try and gather more support for a walk out. They waited for Jean Faut, the manager's wife, to leave first before they talked to the other players.

"Come here girls. I want to talk to you for a minute," Stovroff shouted over the small talk to the remaining players in the smoky clubhouse. "You've probably heard that Shorty has been suspended for a week. Me and Lib have decided to sit out in protest of the suspension. We think the club has acted improperly and imposed too stiff of a penalty on her just for having her spikes off. We're asking all of you to join us in this protest In that way we can get them to listen."

"I don't know. If we walk they will probably suspend us, too," said Dottie Mueller.

"Yeah, I'd like to talk to Karl first," added Jeep Stoll.

"I'm with you guys," said Barbara Hoffman.

Bat girl Carol Moats came running into the clubhouse. "Mr. Winsch wants everyone on the field now!" The freshman at Mishawaka High School scrounged a drag off a cigarette from
Betty Wagoner before she ran back out. At five-foot-ten inches, the dark brown-haired girl was sometimes mistaken

as a player.

Before the game began, Jeep Stoll approached Winsch in the dugout. "I'd really like if you would reconsider your decision and reinstate Shorty. We really need her," she said.

"Sorry, the decision was made to suspend her and I have to stick by that decision."

"Why?"

"I'll tell you why. Because I don't have any choice in the matter. The decision came from a higher authority," he explained.

"I'd like to talk to that higher authority!" she started to get testy with him.

"No!"

"Then I'm joining the others. I think you're giving her a raw deal."

"That's your decision." She turned and left.

The loss of the players had no affect on the Sox in the double-header against Grand Rapids. Jean Faut pitched a three-hit shutout in the first game to lead the Sox 20th victory and her 20th win on the season. In the second game, the Sox took 12 innings to edge the Chicks, 4-3.

After the game, Sue Kidd called her father for advice on whether to join the striking players. He told her she better not join in the dispute. She took his advice and would stay.

Fort Wayne won 9-7 over Rockford the same evening to clinch a tie for the pennant. Their magic number was one. Another win by the Daisies or a loss by the Sox would give the pennant to Fort Wayne.

The Daisies ended the pennant race the next night when they beat Rockford, 5-1. It was the Daisies first pennant in their eight-year history. They would face third-place Rockford in the first round of the playoffs. South Bend would be pitted against fourth-place Grand Rapids.

During the last night of the league on Sunday, September 7, South Bend lost both ends of a doubleheader to their first-round opponent to end up three games behind Fort Wayne in the final standings. The Daisies also lost their doubleheader to their first-round opponent.

Pryer and her group of dissidents managed to talk Barbara Hoffman and Dottie Mueller into walking off the team before the playoffs began. Hoffman had played in the same softball league as Stovroff, so she sided with the strikers.

The Sox recalled Mary Froning, who was on loan to Battle Creek, before the end of the regular season. Going into the Shaughnessy Championship playoffs, the Sox were down to 12 players. Gone was a third of the team. Gone were two outfielders, a second baseman, a third baseman, a first baseman/pitcher and a catcher. Gone was the best base stealer in the league and an All-Star in Pryer. Gone was a home-run hitter in Mueller, who also was an All-Star pitcher at one time. Gone was the best hitter on the team at .301 in Stoll. Gone was the leadership of Mahon, a two time All-Star. Gone was the first-string catcher in Stovroff. About the only player who would not be missed was weak-hitting Hoffman.

South Bend Tribune spouts columnist Joe Doyle compared the loss to the 1952 Yankees losing Mickey Mantle, Yogi Berra, Phil Rizzuto, Allie Reynolds, Gil McDougald and Johnny Mize going into the World Series.

Winsch didn't feel he needed the departed players to win the championship. He figured his wife, who ended the season with a 20-2 record—the best-ever winning percentage in league history—could carry the team in the playoffs. When she wasn't on the mound she could fill in at third base. He also had much of his pitching staff intact: Janet Rumsey, Lou Arnold and Jetty Vincent Mooney. He could call on Betty Wagoner to pitch, too. When the pitchers

weren't on the mound, he could put them elsewhere.
Backup receiver Wimp Baumgartner was quite capable
behind the plate. Marge Wenzell could fill in at second,
third or in the outfield.

A South Bend Tribune reporter dubbed the 12 remaining players as the "dutiful dozen."

Hurricane Charlene and the five tornadoes it spawned
in late August had passed without doing enough damage to
derail the Sox. If anything, the mutiny of a half-dozen
players had brought the remaining dozen players closer
together going into the playoffs.

The top four teams in the league would meet in the
Shaughnessy Playoffs. Only Kalamazoo and last-place
Battle Creek would sit out this dance. The second-place
Blue Sox would face fourth-place Grand Rapids. Meanwhile, Fort Wayne would go against Rockford, which
finished third, 12 games back. The winners of those two
three-game contests would meet for a five-game series.

South Bend did Grand Rapids a favor the last day of
the regular season. The Sox dropped a double dip, 3-0 and
3-1, to the Chicks to allow them to squeak into the playoffs.
The first game of the three-game series would be at
Playland Park. The second and third games would move to
Grand Rapids.

Winsch had few decisions to make about who to start
because he had only 12 players to pick from. He put pitcher
Sue Kidd in right field and pitcher Jetty Vincent Mooney at
second base, Pryer's old position. Marge Wenzell could
play almost anywhere, so he put her at third while his wife
was pitching the first game.

A hot,, humid early September day turned cooler by
game time at 8:15 p.m. After a scoreless first inning, Jean
Faut led off the second with a single. Kidd laid down a
sacrifice bunt to move Faut to second. Gertie Dunn singled

to put runners at the corners. Wenzell hit a grounder to third, which loaded the bases. After a ground out forced Faut at the plate, Betty Wagoner singled to left to score Dunn and put the Sox on top. South Bend added a run in the eighth to take a 2-0 lead.

In the ninth inning, Faut gave up a single to the first batter. The next bailer hit a hot grounder back to her and the ball bounced up over her shoulder for another hit. Then a bunt down the third-base line and a poor throw by Wenzell loaded the bases with nobody out.

Winsch called time and went to the mound to speak to his wife. "Settle down and forget what happened."

"It's my fault the bases are loaded."

"No, it's not. I'm going to change the defense to give you better support in the infield."

"Fine."

"Just act like there's nobody on base and throw strikes."

"Okay."

Winsch had Wenzell and Kidd switch positions, because he knew Kidd would have no trouble throwing to first base unlike Wenzell.

Faut threw strikes and got the next hitter to ground to Joyce Westerman at first base. Westerman fired it home for the force out.

Then the pitcher encouraged clean-up hitter Doris Satterfield to ground out to second base, but a run scored on the fielder's choice.

The run was the first off of Faut in 35 innings dating back to Rockford on August 19.

The pitcher ended the suspense when she got Jean Geissinger to ground out. The players were overjoyed and converged on Faut to congratulate her. Winsch breathed a sigh of relief.

Meanwhile, Fort Wayne was in a tight battle with Rockford that went into extra innings. The Daisies scored in the 10th inning to edge their opponents, 5-4.

Winsch called on Kidd to pitch the second game of the series at Grand Rapids. He put his wife at third and kept Wenzell in right field. In the top of the first, Jo Lenard stole second and scored on an error. The Sox got their second run on a safety squeeze. Faut made it 3-0 when she hit a sacrifice fly to center. By the bottom of the ninth, the Sox led 6-1. However, Kidd walked the first batter. Winsch had her switch positions with his wife and Faut saved the game. The first playoff series was history and the Sox were advancing to the finals.

At the same time the Sox were winning, Fort Wayne was losing. After a 2-0 lead in the first, the Daisies let the Peaches come back and beat them 4-3. The two teams met again after Labor Day and Rockford blanked Fort Wayne, 6-0, on a six-hitter by Mickey Perez Jinright. The series win by Rockford was certainly an upset and surprised a lot of people. But Rockford had pulled out championships twice before over pennant winners.

Now South Bend and Rockford would meet for the 10th championship of the All-American Girls Professional Baseball League.

Now that Fort Wayne had been eliminated, the Sox players and its manager felt they had a better-than-average chance to win the final playoff series with Rockford.

Because Rockford had to vacate its park on Sunday, the five-game series between the Sox and the Peaches would open in Rockford for the first two games and then move to Playland Park for the next two games. Rockford would then have a choice of what field to use for Game Five, if necessary.

The players were quiet on the warm bus ride to

Rockford from South Bend, about a three-hour jaunt. Winsch thought about the line-up for awhile. He would go with his wife on the hill in the first game, so that he could use her later in the series, if necessary. He remembered last year when she was unbeatable in the playoffs and went 4-0. However, his wife had a poor playoff record up until then. She had won two and lost six in previous playoffs. He was confident that she was a better pitcher now than in those previous years and would pull the team through.

Scattered showers danced around the Rockford area and it rained once on the field during the day. The temperature was a mild 70 by game time.

Jacqueline Kelly, 12-11 during the season, was on the hill for the Peaches. Jetty Vincent Mooney got the Sox on the scoreboard in the first. She singled, stole second, went to third on an error and stole home. Faut had trouble with her control and gave up two runs in the second. The Sox tallied for a run in the third. The Peaches continued to hit Faut's offerings and scored a run in each of the next three innings. After Eleanor Callow walloped a Faut offering over the fence for a 7-2 lead, Winsch sent his wife to the showers. The Sox made a threat in the ninth, yet fell short and ended up losing 7-3.

Between the first and second game of the series, Rockford moved the right-field fence in to get the stadium ready for high school football. Winsch saw the difference right away, so he and Ernie Longway, a contractor and member of the Blue Sox Board of Directors, went out and measured the distance. The fence was only 189 feet. Winsch knew the minimum distance to the outfield wall was supposed to be 210 feet, because he had changed his own fences to that distance before the season began.

Winsch approached Peaches manager Bill Allington about the fence at the meeting with the umpires before the game. "Bill, your right field fence is too short."

"No it isn't My ground crew said it was okay."

"I measured it this morning, and it's only 188 feet."

"Really."

"It's not regulation. If a ball is hit over it, it should be a double," Winsch suggested.

"No, it should be a home run. Anyways, it will be the same distance for both teams, so what's the difference?"

"Maybe so, but it should be a double and not a homer. I'm playing this game under protest"

"I want to file a protest, too!" countered Allington. "League rules require a team to have a minimum of 15 players on a team. The Sox only have 12."

"Okay, gentlemen. You'll have to file those protests in writing after the game along with your protest fee," umpire John Anderson told the managers.

Now down 1-0 in the playoffs, Winsch put Janet Rumsey on the mound against Rose Gacioch, Rockford's best pitcher at 20-10 on the season. The clouds gave way to clear skies by game time. The temperature dropped to around 65 degrees. A nice night for baseball.

Gacioch had poor control in the first and walked Mooney.

Lenard then singled. Joyce Westerman hit a grounder to first, which advanced both runners. Faut laced a double to the gap in left-center to score both runners. Rockford scored two runs in the third inning to tie the score.

In the fifth, Rockford's Ruth Richard sent a ball over the controversial fence. Had the fence not been moved in, the ball could have been caught. Winsch was angry at the homer, but glad he had filed his protest. The Sox twice had chances to score only to see them be taken away by good defense. When Rumsey struck out to end the game, the crowd of more than 2,000 fans cheered their team for the last time in the Peach Orchard.

After the game, Winsch followed up his verbal protest

with a letter to the league and a check for $10 from the team to make the protest official. Allington also filed a protest in case the league ruled against him.

Down 2-0, the Sox had their backs up against the wall. One more loss and the season would be over. Some players were beginning to wonder if the loss of six players had been the difference. But Winsch was hopeful that his protest would stand up and the game be replayed.

Immediately before the third game began at Playland Park, league business manager Earl McCammon called for a meeting of the two club owners to discuss the protests. The meeting was still going when the game began.

The Sox jumped out on top in the first inning with a run when Faut knocked in Jo Lenard with a single. Then in the third, Vincent doubled and scored after a sacrifice and an error. Meanwhile, Kidd put down the Peaches in order. The Sox got two more runs in the fourth to take a ~0 lead and send the Cuban hurler to the showers.

Between the fourth and fifth inning, Sox team president Bill Sheehan brought Winsch the news of the protest. "You're protest stands," he explained. "They allowed it because Rockford had refused to discuss the ground rule with you. The game must be replayed."

"It serves them right, since a homer over that fence was the winning margin," Winsch replied. "What about Allington's protest?"

"The way the rule is written, we don't have to have 15 players. We need only nine as a minimum to play a game."

Kidd retired 13 batters in a row before giving up a hit in the fifth. In the eighth, she began to tire and gave up two runs to narrow the score to 4-2. After she gave up a lead-off double in the ninth, Winsch decided he had seen enough. He sent in his wife from third base to finish the game. He called Wenzell in from right field to play third, and he sent

Kidd out to right.

Faut was wild and gave up two runs to tie the score. She settled down after that and the game went to extra innings. In the bottom of the 12th, Kidd singled in Westerman to give the Sox the victory.

Winsch elected to go with Mooney for the third game of the series. Mooney got into hot water in the first inning, but pitched her way out of the jam. However, an error in the second by catcher Wimp Baumgartner allowed the Peaches to take the lead. The receiver continued the dropsies the next inning and allowed another run to score. The Peaches added yet another run in the fourth before the Sox finally scored a run of their own to make it 3-1. But the Peaches added two more in the fifth. The Sox made a comeback that was cut short when Betty Wagoner was thrown out at the plate trying to score from first base on a double to left-center by Mooney. The Peaches held on to win 5-4.

The loss put the Sox in a must-win situation. Winsch was torn between starting his wife and Janet Rumsey. He decided he would hold Faut for the if-necessary game or put her in relief if Rumsey got into trouble. Rockford sent its ace, Gacioch, to the mound in an effort to close out the series in South Bend.

Just as the series had heated up, the weather had turned hot with temperatures in the 90s during the day. Not a lot of people had air conditioning in their homes, so it was an uncomfortable day. The players did as little as possible during the day to save their strength for game time. Many players slept until almost noon. By game time the temperature had cooled to 75, so it was much more bearable for fans and players alike.

Through the first four innings, the game was a pitcher's duel. In the fifth, Rumsey allowed runners to get on first and third with nobody out. Rumsey saw the runner on first leading off farther than she wanted, so she threw over to Westerman. The throw was in the dirt and skirted away from the first baseman. The runner on third scored on the miscue to give the Peaches the lead.

After the seventh-inning stretch, Dunn singled and went to second on an error. She moved to third on a sacrifice and scored on a perfect safety squeeze bunt by Baumgartner. In the eighth Rock-ford loaded the bags. Allington called for a suicide squeeze bunt on a 3-2 count, but Irene Applegren popped up the high-and-inside pitch. Baumgartner tagged the runner coming down the line to complete a double play and squash the rally.

The game went into extra innings. Baumgartner singled to open the tenth. Rumsey laid down a bunt to send her to second. Wagoner hit a grounder to move Baumgartner to third. Mooney walked to load the bases. After a fly out, Westerman smashed a liner to score Baumgartner with the winning run. The series was tied.

Rockford had the choice of fields for the next evening. It chose a men's softball park in Freeport, which had a seating capacity of 2,000. The park was about 30 miles from Rockford. The hot spell continued, as the mercury hit 92 during the day. By game time it cooled to a sticky 78. More fans showed up in Freeport than there were seats, so people were standing everywhere by 8:15 p.m., when the game began. Winsch called on his wife for the finale, while Allington countered with his Cuban hurler.

The Sox struck for a run in the first inning when Westerman doubled to score Vincent. Faut held the Peaches scoreless. Then in the third she came to bat with two on base. She hit a triple to put her team on top 4-0. The manager's wife finally relinquished a run in the fourth inning. But she tripled again in the sixth to give the Sox another run.

Going into the ninth, Faut had a 6-1 lead. She concentrated on throwing strikes. After she gave up a single, Jackie Kelley tripled off of her to right-center. Dottie Key then singled to narrow the score to 6-3. Faut got the next hitter to ground out to retire the side.

Sox players jumped for joy to a chorus of boos from the crowd of some 2,700 fans in the jammed stadium. Winsch hugged his players and his wife in celebration. Then he walked over to the Rockford dugout to shake Allington's hand.

"You had me worried in the ninth inning," Winsch said.

"Your wife was too much for us to handle."

"Yeah, I was saving the best for last."

"You did a hell of a job with just 12 players. I have to respect you for that," Allington said while shaking Winsch's hand.

"Thanks. You did a good job yourself making it to the final series."

"Well, thanks. I appreciate that."

Winsch turned around and joined his players for a photo of the team receiving the championship trophy. League manager Earl McCammon snubbed the manager and presented the trophy to his wife. Winsch could not have cared less. He was happy that his dutiful dozen had overcome the odds and pulled off the second consecutive championship.

# Big baseball fan

**by Gary Henry**

I'm not what you'd call a big baseball fan
Just catch a couple of games now and then when I can
Roughly 12 games a week, a dozen more on weekends
I don't see how that makes me a big baseball fan.

I got a TV in the bathroom so I won't miss a play
By Yankees or Cubbies or even Devil Rays
While standing up in the shower or sitting down on the can
But I wouldn't call myself a big baseball fan.

I'm a human computer for runs batted in
and ERAs too, is that such a sin?
Yet my wife says the season ought to be banned
She acts like I'm some kind of big baseball fan.

Just 'cause I didn't mow the lawn one time this summer
My mind's on the Chisox–if they blow it–a bummer!

That's why I must watch the game and guzzle brew by the
can
I don't think that qualifies me as a big baseball fan.

So I follow the hitters in the 'States and Japan
Ichiro Suzuki to Carlos Beltran
How 'bout those Nippon Ham Fighters, don't you think
they're just grand?
But I don't consider myself a big baseball fan.

Yes I go to the games or I watch on TV
It's part of being American in the land of the free
It's part of being a red-blooded U.S. woman or man!
Though I wouldn't call myself a big baseball fan.

Once the playoffs are over and the Series is done
And I'm sure the team I predicted has handily won
It's time for football–yes! Bucs, Broncos and Rams!
Of course, I don't call myself a big football fan.

*(Henry is a freelance writer and former journalism instruc-
tor in the U.S. Navy.)*

# The back of Chuck Hiller's card

**by David Dixon Margolis**

Slugged first grand slam
by an NL player
in World Series history
in 1962.
(of all guys.)
In '67, led league in pinch hits.
First guy I ever knew of
that I would describe
as horse-faced.
Big prominent nostrils
that scared me a bit.
Acquired from Giants to fill gap
left by Ron Hunt, who suffered
a separated shoulder
in collision with Cards' Phil Gagliano.
We never forgave Gagliano for that,

my brother and I.
Never.
Not even now.
Hiller was like your stepfather.
It wasn't his fault he was there,
but he was a daily reminder
of what you were missing,
what you really wanted.
Slugged first homer
by an NL player
in World Series history
in 1962.
And they can never take that away from him.
That or the horse-faced thing.

*(Margolis is a member of the Society for American Base-*
*ball Research.)*

# Baseball not always first

**by W.C. Madden**

When Kent Mercker took the mound against the Texas Rangers on May 11, 2000, he knew something wasn't right. He had a headache that he thought was a migraine at first. By the time he got to the second inning, the pain intensified.

After one out in the second, the lefthander felt dizzy and the pain in his head was too much to bear. He went to one knee after a pitch. His teammates and manager came to see what was wrong and he was taken out of the game.

The Anaheim Angels hurler was taken to UCI Medical Center, where a CAT scan and anteriogram were performed. The tests revealed that he suffered a brain hemotoma. He was bleeding in the brain, but futher tests didn't reveal an aneurysm.

The Angels placed him on the disabled list on May 12. For four days he laid in intensive care under complete darkness.

Baseball was the furthest thing from his mind. He was thinking of his family.

Three months to the day after the brain injury, Mercker was back on the mound against the New York Yankees. He was fully recovered and his chances for another incident was almost nonexistent.

# Who's on first?

**by Bud Abbott and Lou Costello**

**Abbott:** Well Costello, I'm going to New York with you. The Yankee's manager gave me a job as coach for as long as your on the team.

**Costello:** Look Abbott, if you're the coach, you must know all the players.

**Abbott:** I certainly do.

**Costello:** Well you know I've not met the guys. So you'll have to tell me their names, and then I'll know who's playing on the team.

**Abbott:** Oh, I'll tell you their names, but you know it seems to me they give these ball players now-a-days very peculiar names.

**Costello:** You mean funny names?

**Abbott:** Strange names, pet names...like Dizzy Dean...

**Costello:** His brother Daffy

**Abbott:** Daffy Dean...

**Costello:** And their French cousin.

**Abbott:** French?

**Costello:** Goofe'

**Abbott:** Goofe' Dean. Well, let's see, we have on the bags, Who's on first, What's on second, I Don't Know is on third...

**Costello:** That's what I want to find out.

**Abbott:** I say Who's on first, What's on second, I Don't Know's on third.

**Costello:** Are you the manager?

**Abbott:** Yes.

**Costello:** You gonna be the coach too?

**Abbott:** Yes.

**Costello:** And you don't know the fellows' names.

**Abbott:** Well I should.

**Costello:** Well then who's on first?

**Abbott:** Yes.

**Costello:** I mean the fellow's name.

**Abbott:** Who.

**Costello:** The guy on first.

**Abbott:** Who.

**Costello:** The first baseman.

**Abbott:** Who.

**Costello:** The guy playing...

**Abbott:** Who is on first!

**Costello:** I'm asking you who's on first.

**Abbott:** That's the man's name.

**Costello:** That's who's name?

**Abbott:** Yes.

**Costello:** Well go ahead and tell me.

**Abbott:** That's it.

**Costello:** That's who?

**Abbott:** Yes.

*Pause*

**Costello:** Look, you gotta first baseman?

**Abbott:** Certainly.

**Costello:** Who's playing first?

**Abbott:** That's right.

**Costello:** When you pay off the first baseman every month, who gets the money?

**Abbott:** Every dollar of it.

**Costello:** All I'm trying to find out is the fellow's name on first base.

**Abbott:** Who.

**Costello:** The guy that gets...

**Abbott:** That's it.

**Costello:** Who gets the money...

**Abbott:** He does, every dollar of it. Sometimes his wife comes down and collects it.

**Costello:** Who's wife?

**Abbott:** Yes.

*Pause*

**Abbott:** What's wrong with that?

**Costello:** what I wanna know is when you sign up the first baseman, how does he sign his name?

**Abbott:** Who.

**Costello:** The guy.

**Abbott:** Who.

**Costello:** How does he sign...

**Abbott:** That's how he signs it.

**Costello:** Who?

**Abbott:** Yes.

*Pause*

**Costello:** All I'm trying to find out is what's the guy's name on first base.

**Abbott:** No. What is on second base.

**Costello:** I'm not asking you who's on second.

**Abbott:** Who's on first.

**Costello:** One base at a time!

**Abbott:** Well, don't change the players around.

**Costello:** I'm not changing nobody!

**Abbott:** Take it easy, buddy.

**Costello:** I'm only asking you, who's the guy on first base?

**Abbott:** That's right.

**Costello:** Ok.

**Abbott:** All right.

*Pause*

**Costello:** What's the guy's name on first base?

**Abbott:** No. What is on second.

**Costello:** I'm not asking you who's on second.

**Abbott:** Who's on first.

**Costello:** I don't know.

**Abbott:** He's on third, we're not talking about him.

**Costello:** Now how did I get on third base?

**Abbott:** Why you mentioned his name.

**Costello:** If I mentioned the third baseman's name, who did I say is playing third?

**Abbott:** No. Who's playing first.

**Costello:** What's on base?

**Abbott:** What's on second.

**Costello:** I don't know.

**Abbott:** He's on third.

**Costello:** There I go, back on third again!

*Pause*

**Costello:** Would you just stay on third base and don't go off it.

**Abbott:** All right, what do you want to know?

**Costello:** Now who's playing third base?

**Abbott:** Why do you insist on putting Who on third base?

**Costello:** What am I putting on third.

**Abbott:** No. What is on second.

**Costello:** You don't want who on second?

**Abbott:** Who is on first.

**Costello:** I don't know.

**Together:** Third base!

*Pause*

**Costello:** Look, you gotta outfield?

**Abbott:** Sure.

**Costello:** The left fielder's name?

**Abbott:** Why.

**Costello:** I just thought I'd ask you.

**Abbott:** Well, I just thought I'd tell ya.

**Costello:** Then tell me who's playing left field.

**Abbott:** Who's playing first.

**Costello:** I'm not...stay out of the infield!!! I want to know what's the guy's name in left field?

**Abbott:** No, What is on second.

**Costello:** I'm not asking you who's on second.

**Abbott:** Who's on first!

**Costello:** I don't know.

**Together:** Third base!

*Pause*

**Costello:** The left fielder's name?

**Abbott:** Why.

**Costello:** Because!

**Abbott:** Oh, he's center field.

*Pause*

**Costello:** Look, You gotta pitcher on this team?

**Abbott:** Sure.

**Costello:** The pitcher's name?

**Abbott:** Tomorrow.

**Costello:** You don't want to tell me today?

**Abbott:** I'm telling you now.

**Costello:** Then go ahead.

**Abbott:** Tomorrow!

**Costello:** What time?

**Abbott:** What time what?

**Costello:** What time tomorrow are you gonna tell me who's pitching?

**Abbott:** Now listen. Who is not pitching.

**Costello:** I'll break your arm if you say who's on first!!! I want to know what's the pitcher's name?

**Abbott:** What's on second.

**Costello:** I don't know.

**Together:** Third base!

*Pause*

**Costello:** Gotta a catcher?

**Abbott:** Certainly.

**Costello:** The catcher's name?

**Abbott:** Today.

**Costello:** Today, and tomorrow's pitching.

**Abbott:** Now you've got it.

**Costello:** All we got is a couple of days on the team.

*Pause*

**Costello:** You know I'm a catcher too.

**Abbott:** So they tell me.

**Costello:** I get behind the plate to do some fancy catching, Tomorrow's pitching on my team and a heavy hitter gets up. Now the heavy hitter bunts the ball. When he bunts the ball, me, being a good catcher, I'm gonna throw the guy out at first. So I pick up the ball and throw it to who?

**Abbott:** Now that's the first thing you've said right.

**Costello:** I don't even know what I'm talking about!

*Pause*

**Abbott:** That's all you have to do.

**Costello:** Is to throw the ball to first base.

**Abbott:** Yes!

**Costello:** Now who's got it?

**Abbott:** Naturally.

*Pause*

**Costello:** Look, if I throw the ball to first base, somebody's gotta get it. Now who has it?

**Abbott:** Naturally.

**Costello:** Who?

**Abbott:** Naturally.

**Costello:** Naturally?

**Abbott:** Naturally.

**Costello:** So I pick up the ball and I throw it to Naturally.

**Abbott:** No you don't you throw the ball to Who.

**Costello:** Naturally.

**Abbott:** That's different.

**Costello:** That's what I said.

**Abbott:** Your not saying it...

**Costello:** I throw the ball to Naturally.

**Abbott:** You throw it to Who.

**Costello:** Naturally.

**Abbott:** That's it.

**Costello:** That's what I said!

**Abbott:** You ask me.

**Costello:** I throw the ball to who?

**Abbott:** Naturally.

**Costello:** Now you ask me.

**Abbott:** You throw the ball to Who?

**Costello:** Naturally.

**Abbott:** That's it.

**Costello:** Same as you! Same as YOU!!! I throw the ball to who. Whoever it is drops the ball and the guy runs to second. Who picks up the ball and throws it to What. What throws it to I Don't Know. I Don't Know throws it back to Tomorrow, Triple play. Another guy gets up and hits a long fly ball to Because. Why? I don't know! He's on third and I don't give a darn!

**Abbott:** What?

**Costello:** I said I don't give a darn!

**Abbott:** Oh, that's our shortstop.

*(Editor's Note: Their most famous vaudeville act—a farcical baseball commentary—was also performed on radio and television, and it was made into a popular recording.*

# At the baseball game

**By Joan M. Thomas**

For approximately one hundred and eighty minutes,
I find magic in my life. I find it at the baseball game. All
the sweet memories of my youth spring alive. Though each
game offers no promise of a joyous ending, or even a
thrilling, but disappointing defeat, I relish every aspect of
the ambience.

Modern cynics try to dispel our long cherished
notion that baseball serves as a metaphor for life. I know
better. It's even more. For nine innings or more, it is life.
From the moment I click through the turnstile, I join the
mass of humanity with a common cause.

The scorecard barker's call beckons us, one and all,
like the clanging recess bell from my long gone grammar
school. The aroma of broiling hot dogs weaves its way to
my greatful nostrils. Though the ballparks are larger, and
the players and owners are greedier today, those little
sausages, browning and sweating delectable juices meant to

mingle with tangy yellow mustard, taste as good as ever. Better, perhaps.

With my scorecard tucked carefully under my arm, I purchase this ballpark delicacy along with an icy cold cola to enhance my dining pleasure. I study my ticket stub to determine the location of my assigned seat. As I pass through the entranceway, I am greeted by the overwhelming brilliance of green grass. As I search for the correct seating area, the voice of the public address announcer reverberates indistinguishable words, presumably English. It doesn't matter.

Arriving early, 1 welcome the sounds of batting practice. Horsehide strikes wood. Crack! Tchaikovsky's *1812 Overture* ended with cannons sounding, a dramatic climax to be sure. My day at the ballpark begins with this percussion. It's splendid music to me.

So, happily juggling my American gourmet lunch and simple documenting tool: a freshly sharpened pencil bearing the home team's name and colors, I settle in for the duration. More attendees filter in, representing a cross section of the country that gave birth to this game long before any of us entered the scene.

Then, the announcer's words suddenly, *magically,* become perfectly clear. He proclaims the starting lineup. After that, the event that unites us all under the sun, the singing of the National Anthem, commences. I can never quite finish it. I always get to the point where everyone drags out the "star spangled banner wave..." Just when I reach "spangled," that lump lying dormant in my throat through every other emotionally charged moment in my life: graduations, birthdays, Christmas, family reunions, emerges.

That debilitating lump first arose when I joined in the singing at my hometown, small town ballpark some forty-five years ago. It seems that we all just have a difficult time getting past the "banner" part. Is it "baan-er-er-er ye-et wave," or is it "ba-aa-aa-ner-er y~et wave?" Regardless, the following final words come out strong and clear. After "the land of the free and the home of the brave," a mighty cheer envelopes the stadium. As if we're glad we got through it again, and we can get down to seeing a ballgame. And that's what germinates the lump in my throat. I haven't finished the song with the crowd since 1955. The team takes the field and the game starts. I regain my composure. The tear in my eye vanishes, and the ornery lump disappears.

The lady in front of me spoils her son with souvenirs and concessions. But he's more interested in watching the game. An ancient gentleman to my left mutters about the juiced-up ball and the need for pitching. Two young couples behind us enjoy themselves thoroughly. Eating, drinking and cheering, they hope for a victory.

The club mascot wanders through the crowd, providing amusement for those who only came to be amused. I tolerate that, as I know it took a long time for me to appreciate the greatness of this sport. Every inning brings a new edition to the annals. Every pitch, if frozen in time, could represent a work of art. The beer and soda vendors hail their offerings, and the crowd roars with each exciting occurrence on the field. Sometimes the innings drag and the fans grow restless. My companion of thirty years, my husband, grumbles about the manager's decision, a player's performance, and the inattention of some of the fans. It's all part of the symphony with the unpredictable finale.

Finally, that big play grabs the attention of all eyes present. A stolen base; a double play; a spectacular catch; a home run; earns the roar of approval from a diverse group. For that brief peried, we are one.

I'm happier when our team wins. But of course, that

can't always happen. Even after a loss, I go home renewed. Nothing beats the blues like a day at the baseball park.

*(Thomas is a freelance writer from St. Louis.)*

# Mickey's grand slam

**by Michael E. Del Duco**

Mickey had a baseball game one crystal clear day,
so he put on his uniform and was on his way.

He kiddingly said he would hit a grand slam,
off the left-handed pitcher named Sam.

Mickey played shortstop and he wasn't too bad,
but when a ball went 'tween his legs, he got mad.

Mickey's team was always used to winning,
but the other team scored three the first inning.

Well, it got to be the bottom of the ninth, and the score was
three to zip.
So, it looked like Mickey was going down on a slow
sinking ship.

The pitcher walked the first three men, the next two struck
out.
Up to the bat came Mickey, and the crowd began to shout.

The pitcher threw a strike, but Mickey did not care.
He knew he wouldn't strike out—he would not dare.

The next pitch was a slider, and Mickey hit the ball a mile,
but the umpire cried foul ball and the pitcher let out a
smile.

Mickey wasn't worried, he wasn't scared at all.
The next pitch was low and the ump called it a ball.

Mickey was determined that he would not fail.
The next ball was down the middle and he let is sail.

He ran around the bases, and watched the ball.
He cried, "Grand Slam!" as it flew across the wall.

Mickey headed for home plate, his face was all a gleam.
When suddenly he woke up and said, "Man, what a
dream!"

*(Del Duco is a freelance writer from Sterling Heights,
Michigan.)*

# Sosa rocks!

by **W.C. Madden**

Hickory, dickory dock;
This Sosa guy can sock,
He cracks the ball,
against the wall,
and makes the bleachers rock!

**Thurman Munson**

# Some died before their time

**by W.C. Madden**

Everyone dies. That's a given. When is the unknown factor unless the event is planned. A few deaths in baseball have come long before life expectancy and caught many by surprise.

Babe Ruth received much of the recognition for the Yankees being the best team in baseball for a long time, but also in the supporting cast was another great player–**Lou Gehrig**. Gehrig took over first base in 1925 and began a streak of consecutive games. He became known as the Iron Man of Baseball.

Ruth departed the Yankees in 1934 and Gehrig picked up where Ruth left off. Then suddenly his performance began to drop off. He wasn't himself. He felt tired and weak. Doctors thought he had a gall bladder problem.

In the spring of 1939, his performance on the field became less than professional. He fielded poorly and hit like a weakling. Something was terribly wrong. On May 1,

Gehrig pulled himself out of the lineup for the first time in 14 years. His steak of 2,130 consecutive games was broken. He was examined at the Mayo Clinic. His diagnosis was amyotrophic lateral sclerosis (ALS), an incurable disease that attacked the motor pathways and cells of the central nervous system. ALS would become known as Lou Gehrig's Disease after that.

On July 4, the Yankees held an Appreciation Day for the slugger at Yankee Stadium. He spoke to the crowd in a tearful address. "I may have been given a bad break, but...I consider myself the luckiest man on the face of the earth," he said to the crowd. He will always be remembered for those words.

The National Baseball Hall of Fame waived the five-year waiting period and inducted Gehrig that summer. He passed away on June 2, 1941. He was 37.

The Baseball Hall of Fame also waived the five-year waiting period for another player who died during the midst of a famed career–**Roberto Clemente**. In 18 seasons in the major leagues, he was a 12-time all-star. The Puerto Rican player also won a dozen Gold Gloves and four batting titles. He was the National League's Most Valuable Player, and in 1971 he led the Pirates to victory in the World Series and earned the Series MVP award.

Besides being a great player, he was known as a great humanitarian. In December 1972, Nicaragua suffered a devastating earthquake that killed more than 6,000 people. Clemente helped raise money for supplies to the Central American nation. "Anytime you have an opportunity to make things better and you don't, then you are wasting your time on this Earth," he once said.

When he heard that some supplies weren't getting through, he rented a DC-7 to fly supplies there himself from Puerto Rico on December 31. His plane crashed shortly after takeoff and he perished.

Clemente's memory lives on with the Roberto Clemente Man of the Year Award, presented by John Hancock. It is given each year to the Major League Baseball player who combines outstanding skills on the baseball field with devoted work in the community. Clemente became the first Latin player to be inducted into the Hall of Fame.

Another player who perished in a plane crash was **Thurman Munson**, a catcher for the New York Yankees. On August 2, 1979, Munson's twin-engine jet fell short of the runway during an attempted landing at the Akron-Canton airfield. He was practicing his takeoffs and landings when his plane hit a tree. He was trapped inside the burning plane and died. He was 32.

Considered my most as the best catcher in the American League in the 1970s. The first-round draft started his major league career winning the American League Rookie of the Year award in 1970. The six-time All-Star appeared in three consecutive World Series appearances in 1976, 1977, and 1978, and hit .529, .320 and .320, respectively. In 1976, Munson led the Yankees into the World Series and earned Most Valuable Player honors in the American League.

Following his death in 1979, the Yankees honored Munson by retiring his uniform number (15) and placing a memorial plaque on the center field wall at Yankee stadium. Although he is not an official member of Baseball's Hall of Fame, a re-creation of Munson's locker, including spikes, glove, and jersey, has been preserved in Cooperstown.

The Colorado Rockies had high hopes for pitcher **Doug Million** and paid him nearly a million dollars after drafting him in the first round in 1994. They knew he had asthma, but they were willing to take the risk. In 1997, the pitcher was a disappointment, but the Rockies kept working with him.

On September 23, Million was at a Mesa, Arizona, area restaurant playing a television trivia game with minor-league pitcher Jason Romine when he suffered an asthma attack. Romine called 911. Emergency medical personnel lost Million's pulse in the ambulance on the way to a hospital. Doctors worked in vain for 45 minutes to resuscitate him, and he was pronounced dead shortly after 3 a.m.

Bob Genhard, Rockies' Executive Vice President and General Manager, had to break the news to Colorado players before they took the field against San Francisco. Many of the players broke down in tears. The Rockies held a moment of silence in Million's memory before the game.

"Life is not fair, and he just got cheated," his father, Dave, told a newspaper.

Another minor league player who died unexpectedly was **Tom Maggard**. Drafted by the Boston Red Sox, Maggard made his way up to Triple-A before he died from an insect bite. Doctors never determined who the culprit was.

Another tragedy occurred on Opening Day in 1995. Seven pitched into the season, umpire **John McSherry** stepped back from his position behind the plate and collapsed. He died on the field. The huge umpire suffered a massive heart attack. He was 51. The game was cancelled.

The son of an Irish immigrant had umpired in the majors since 1971. He had turned into an excellent and well-respected umpire through the years.

A year after umpire McSherry died, the Cincinnati Reds dedicated a room in his memory and eulogized him as "an umpire's umpire."

McSherry is not the only participant in history of the majors to die during a contest.

However, there were two players in the history of the game that died from injuries sustained during a game.

The first was **Mike "Doc" Powers**. The catcher for the Philadelphia Athletics was playing in the inaugural contest at Shibe Park on April 12, 1909. The receiver went after a foul ball and collided with the wall. He died 14 days later from internal injuries that he suffered from the game. The second player was **Ray Chapman**. On August 17, 1920, the Cleveland Indians shortstop stepped up to the plate at New York's Polo Grounds. Submarine pitcher Carl Mays fired a pitch that carried inside and struck Chapman in the left temple. The ball hit with such force that it came bounding back to Mays, who threw it to first for what he though was an out. It was an out all right. Lights out for Chapman. The umpire called for a doctor. The team physician applied ice and Chapman stood to the relief of the crowed. However, on his way to the center field clubhouse he collapsed. He was then taken off the field by stretcher. Twelve hours later he died.

Some players play like there's no tomorrow. That might be the best way considering you never know about what tomorrow holds.

# Prayer

**by Edmund Vance Cooke**

The score was a tie;
Flick popped a fly;
Harry went down on four;
Turner gave him a leg
To the second peg
And we had just one chance more.
Five thousand prayers to heave mounted;
(Five thousand had the turnstile counted.)

"O, Thou who heed'st the sparrow's fall
   And numberest every hair,
Look down upon this game of ball
   And hearken to our prayer.
Deem us not impious, for more
Than sparrows to us is the score.

Grant us, oh, grant us but a bingle,

E'en tho' it be a scratchy single,
If doubles be too rare.
Make sure the batter's arm and eye
And guard him from the foul too high,
For more to us a long, low fly
Than many a numbered hair."
And behold; the soul of the Player heard,
A latent prowess in him stirred;
Bing! and the ball flew like a bird,
Nor stopped it till he touched at third!
Nor that's the effect of prayer.
For prayer is potent, if it find.
The ready arm, the willing mind.

Another day, another game,
The situation much the same;
Again the prayer arose:
A Mucker (for I would not name
An erring player to his shame)
Stood teetering on his toes,
And when he heard the ascending shout,
The stomach of his soul fell out.
Thrice on his clammy hands he spat,
And thrice he swung the harmless bat
And thrice he split the air,
Swept off his balance by the force
Which should have spurred him on his course,
For that's the effect of prayer.

For prayer, my friends, was never meant
To supersede the instrument.

*(Reprinted from Baseballogy, 1912.)*

# My coach, Spagger

**by Mark W. Schraf**

It didn't exist in my family. Or, to be more precise, death
was not acknowledged when I was growing up. When my
Dad passed away I was seven. My Mom really did a great
job of raising me and my sister by herself, caring for our
ills and wounds, both external and internal. But mortality
was simply, totally, unequivocally denied. She's always
referred to Dad as "asleep with the angels." Always. We
were forbidden to watch "Bambi." I'm not kidding. But in
her misguided attempts to shield her children from the
inevitable anguish of losing people they love, she helped
create a semi-neurotic.

     My high school baseball team was like most high
school baseball teams: the cliques were thick, the talent
pool shallow as a politician's promise, and the coach cared
a lot more than the players did. I'd always been pretty big,
like my Dad, they said, and while I could throw pretty hard,

my control was suspect. Actually, I had relatively good command. I just couldn't bring myself to throw a pitch inside to anyone. Everything was either an outside strike or a ball. Once the hitters realized this, I'd either walk the ballpark or get tattooed.

Coach Spagnola wanted everyone to call him "Spagger," but no one ever did. A large man with an ever-growing paunch, a jowly, pock-marked face, and a hawkish nose set off by a Marines-style, totally unfashionable crew cut. He was the kind of adult that you'd never look in the eye, because he'd never demand it of you. He'd start off every practice with a story about some game that the Cleveland Indians played in the 60's, a story intended to sail toward the safe harbor of solid, fundamental baseball instruction. But he always seemed to veer off coursetoward the rocky, inane shallows of a morality lesson.

"Come on, men!" he'd bellow. He always called us men, although we all knew we weren't men, not even close to it "You gotta work, work, work! You gotta be thinking all the time out there! That's what Gary Bell did against the Senators!" It was embarrassing. It galvanized the team into a single unit dedicated to the adolescent pursuit of detached apathy.

I was 19. A most self-centered, self-righteous, selfish age. A sophomore in college on summer break, I was a walking cliche, just as all freshman know that they know nothing and all sophomores know that they now know everything. Coach Spagnola decided early in my senior year that I was his guy. That's what he called me, "his guy," as in "You're my guy, Scott. I'm gonna make you into the next Sudden Sam." To this day I have no idea why he picked me.

Ennis had a better fastball, a curve, which I didn't, and he was a much better athlete than I was. So were Jerry Thomas and Eric Wolinski and about half a dozen other

guys. Still, he picked me. He'd tell the team that they
should watch me. Learn from me! Cripes, I didn't know
what the hell I was doing out there most of the time, and
the team is supposed to follow my example? It would've
been laughable, except none of my teammates laughed.
They were pissed. I was a suck-up. I was Coach's "butt
buddy." I tried to tell them that I didn't like him either, that
I couldn't figure it out, didn't know why he liked me so
much. They didn't believe me. I guess I wouldn't have
believed me either. We were pretty pathetic that year.
Coach would send me out there every third game, and I'd
either walk half the team or get shelled or both, and he'd
come out to the mound to put me out of my misery and say,
loud enough for the infield to hear, "Not you, Scott. These
bunch of worthless bastards didn't give you shit for support." Not exactly the ideal team spirit builder. But my
performance was irrelevant. I was his guy, even though I
had no idea who "Sudden Sam" was.

    After my senior season mercifully ended, Coach
said he'd been talking to a friend of his at the University,
that he'd arranged a tryout for me. "I put in the good word
for yah, big guy. Just go up there and mow 'em down like I
know you can. Like Sudden Sam." I could only look at him.
I wanted to ask him how he could have so much faith in me
when I obviously had so little in myself, but I never said a
word. Never went to the tryout, either. What was the point.
I could've stopped by his house, or visited him in the
hospital, or even dropped him a card, but I did none of
them. I was 19. Coach was gone a few months later, just
after I'd returned to school. Cancer. Just like my Dad. I've
often wondered since how he felt, how I made him feel that
    Sunday. I wonder if that slap I gave him made him
remember, when he was desperately trying to forget, the
numbing chill of his life being squeezed out of him, that he
was slowly being erased. I wonder if he felt as if he were

was slowly being erased. I wonder if he felt as if he were already gone. After all, through my eyes, I had told him he already was. So long Spagger. Stay warm.

*(Schraf is a member of the Society for American Baseball Research and fiction editor for Spitball Magazine.)*

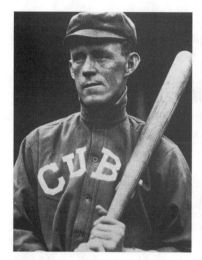

**Johnny Evers**            **Joe Tinker**

# Baseball's sad lexicon

**by Franklin P. Adams**

These are the saddest of possible words:
  "Tinkers to Evers to Chance."
Trio of bear cubs, and fleeter than birds,
  Tinkers to Evers to Chance.
Ruthlessly pricking our gonfalon bubble,
Making a Giant hit into a double–
Words that are heavy with nothing but trouble:
  "Tinkers to Evers to Chance."

**Frank Chance**

# The diary of Frank Chance

## by C. Brooke Rothwell

**1905**

It was a great honor to take the helm of the Chicago Cubs!
Frank Selee had put together a truly wonderful physical and
mental quilt work-a psychological masterpiece stitched
over the years. Steinfeldt was the final patch. This band of
fierce warriors I was proud to lead! I remember putting on
the uniform and thinking of the knights and their armor
projecting a fierce protective shield like the Cubs logo and
our colors of battle and our spikes of steel. Our caps fit like
skin on a skull and the 'C' emblaonzed upon the crown
reminded me of the lamp on the courageous coal miner's
cap as they Illuminated the caverns of the unknown... as we
would explore the mysteries of hand/eye coordination and

master the art of hitting 500 and playing pennate (sic)
winning ball on the emerald diamond above ground!

**1906**
All I remember about the first games was the sweet smell
of our new gloves which we all pounded with our bats until
nice and soft. The aroma of the shaved grass and fresh
milled pine for the new bleachers and box seats and the
saps who were sure to sit on the sap. Clouds of cigar smoke
billowed from the grandstands as the band played marches
and me and Rehulebach would search the stands for ladies
in those damn Merry Widow hats and case the crowd for
loudmouth drunks who might be trouble later on. All I
remember was the umpire going from left to right announc-
ing the line ups. The blood began to cartwheel in my ears..
Then it was over and the war began.

**1908**
Spring training was always a feast after starving. The
baseball ribs of my boys were showing through their
undershirts by the time we got to Florida. The weather, like
the flora and fauna, was fantastic when around dusk the
silhouette of clouds in the distance were illuminated by
heat lightning that exploded like cannons of antiquity in a
classic battle for the mind of man which had nothing on the
matchups between me and McGraw. I always assumed no
one wanted to win like me until I met McGraw. It was as if
this person was created out of my imagination to appear
before me as a competitive challenger of epic proportions
hitherto unseen outside the ancient colosseum (sic). West
Side Park and The Polo Grounds were true Civil War
battlegrounds..

**1909**
1908 was the season everyone wanted our hide. We proved

that the '06 Series loss to the Sox was a damn shame. Personally, I took '07 on the head for a third of the season but the boys didn't miss me and we won by 17 games. The series was ours and boy did we woop it up in grand style at the Astoria with a victory celebration. But '08 was earned like proof in the pudding. On THAT day, oh that day, McGraw should have known better than to let ANY detail come between him and the pennant; Evers checkmated the Pirates with the same kind of play on Gill a few weeks before. That splash got papers wet in every city. And who was umpire that day? The same Hank O'Day! Isn't the first thing you learn is to run out every play? I mean *every* play! Hell, I've had to slug my way back to the bench lots of times with pocket knives flashing and broken bottles at my back. You run out everything just in case. Besides, Tin-Man McGinnity tried throwing the ball away which is interference. McGraw knew I knew he knew better. He looked like he swallowed a clock! That season was the top of the mountain of my life and these of my men. The World Series was serious fun. We took out our-pliers and de-clawed those bengals! Beating Cobb was like beating the Tigers twice which by the way is what nobody else had done before–two series in a row that is. I'll never forget Cobb screaming from the dugout steps after the last out of game five: "You can all grow cunt in your thighs and fuck yourselves!" Son of a senator, he acted like he had unlim-ited access to the speedballs in Papa's cabinet.

## 1910

For me it came down to defense. Pitching was of course our front line but it really came down to catching the ball. Stay in front of it no matter what and squeeze it. At the slightest provocation take the extra base because even if the throw is true the chance of it being caught is not sure. Force their hand and make them play perfect ball. When they

know you play this way, no quarters barred they know
they're up against it. They will fold. Maybe not today but
later when it counts. I've seen the shutters snap shut in the
eyes of guys who knew we weren't going to beat ourselves.
Lights out gentlemen! Game called on account of darkness
of the soul...

**1911**
It was never about money. I had money. In baseball money
means respect. I had to fight for recognition of my ability
and talent and I should not have had to. There are people
you can talk to and others one must use his fists upon. With
me you got respect if you gave it. If you were unreasonable
you found out immediately where you stood with me. I
didn't care if you were the owner; opposing players, the
fans or my own men. Justice from my fists was the last card
I'd play in a rough game. The golden rule isn't golden for
no good reason. It applies whether one applies it or not!

*(Rothwell is a member of the Society for American Base-
ball Research.)*

# Team Trivia Quiz

Guess the Major League team from the following clues. Answers at the end of the book. *(Contributed by Mark Sommer, a Society for American Baseball Research member.)*

1. The artful ones          _____
2. Commies                  _____
3. Developed film           _____
4. Calcutta natives         _____
5. Friar Tuck               _____
6. Goliath, King Kong       _____
7. Pope electors            _____
8. Fearless ones            _____
9. Female equines           _____
10. Don't wear with formal  _____
11. Western hills           _____
12. Fire spotters           _____
13. One was really old      _____
14. Beer makers             _____
15. Deep blues              _____
16. Teeth that have been extracted  _____
17. Santa fills them        _____
18. Some have fallen        _____
19. Captain Hook and friends  _____
20. Rattlers                _____
21. Romulus and Remus       _____
22. Belonging to George Jetson's pet  _____
23. Several Opera houses    _____
24. Eastern bird            _____
25. Calcutta cats           _____
26. Types of supporters     _____
27. Bad sting               _____
28. Sport fishes            _____
29. Baby bears              _____
30. Sad birds               _____

# Such is life

**by Lester Raymond Cash**

When he was young and frisky he was thought to be a star,
The hero of the bleachers and the toast of every bar.
The fans all clustered 'round when he appeared upon the
street,
(The sight of him in public was considered quite a treat.)
The turnstiles clicked quite merrily when he was in the
game,
The magnates made a fortune cashing in upon his fame.
But now he is a dub, his days of glory now are past,
For he's a Big League manager and his team came in last.

*(Reprinted from Baseball Magazine, March 1926.)*

# Making a difference

**by W.C. Madden**

In 1997, Eric Davis seemed headed toward one of his best seasons in the majors as he led the American League in batting with a .388 average. Then he suffered severe stomach cramps and had to be pulled out of the lineup.

Doctors discovered a mass in his colon. Cancer. It was removed along with a third of his colon. His career could be over. He began chemotherapy in July. To make matters worse, Eric's brother died in August. But the all-star athlete was determined to return to baseball that season and came off the disabled list in mid-September.

The Orioles put the brave player back in the lineup a day after going through another chemo session. Davis responded with a 4-for-5 performance, including his first homer since May. Then he helped his team to an Eastern Division crown.

Davis' devotion to the sport was honored with the

Hutch Award and Roberto Clemente Award. "I'm no different than any other cancer patient, except I'm a public figure," he said. " Hopefully because of this, I can increase the public's awareness regarding testing and precautions for colon cancer."

He has since become a spokesman and leader in letting the public know about his disease. Davis has also helped to revive baseball in the inner city.

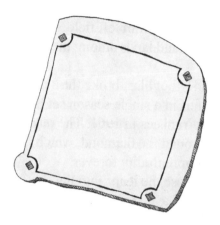

# Four bases for history

**by Joel Barnhart**

The pitcher stands on the mound, sweat dripping from beneath his blue-and-red cap. He looks at the batter. He quivers slightly. For the man he must face is no ordinary man. He must face the Goliath of baseball. He must face Mark McGwire, the first baseman of the St. Louis Cardinals.

The pitcher, Steve Traschel of the Chicago Cubs, squints at his catcher, Scott Servais, who gives him the sign. Traschel nods his head in agreement of the pitch and sets. He rears his body back then releases his first pitch to the Beast of St. Louis.

McGwire's face is overcome with an expression of aggression and pure power, as he lashes his 34-inch, 33-ounce bat at the rounded white sphere headed his way. The bat meets the ball and the crack of the wood is heard seemingly throughout the entire city. A mighty and deafening roar comes from the sellout crowd at Busch Stadium on

this muggy St. Louis evening. The round white ball is
shown rockets toward the outfield wall in left field. The
ball barely clears the green wall and lands among the
batting cages.

He has done it. The 341-foot blast broke the 37-
year-old record of 61 home runs in a single season set by
Roger Maris of the New York Yankees in 1961. The record
is his to treasure for the trip around the diamond, which
will seal his place in baseball immortality forever.

As Mark heads to first base, he leaps into the
embrace of his first base coach, Dave McKay. However, in
his haste, McGwire misses the first base bag, and is di-
rected by McKay to go back and make certain that he
touches the bag. Mark quickly backs up and places his size
13 red cleats into the base. He then heads toward second
base. As he passes by, Chicago first baseman Mark Grace,
an opponent of McGwire on this night and previously in
college, extends his fist for a "punch" of congratulations
for the man of the moment. McGwire obliges and continues
on his way to the next brief stop, second base. It is there
that he receives a high five and pat on the back from Cubs'
second sacker Mickey Morandini. He firmly plants his foot
into the bag, and continues this magical journey around the
diamond.

Before he reaches third, McGwire takes a brief moment to
high five Chicago shortstop Jose Hernandez. He then gives
a salute to a man who was teammate earlier in the season,
the veteran third baseman Gary Gaetti. Gaetti accepts the
salute and then pumps his fist in the air to cheer his friend.
As Mark gets to third, he briefly stops to hug Gaetti and
give him a high five as well. As he rounds third, he slaps
the outstretched hand of St. Louis' third base coach and
former Oakland Athletics' teammate, Carney Lansford.
McGwire now has less than 90 feet separating him from
legend. When he nears the final base, the big man points to

the sky and blows a brief kiss heavenward to Roger Maris, who passed away in 1985. McGwire stops and wraps his massive white and red uniformed body around the gray and blue of the Chicago catcher. After a few words for Scott, McGwire proudly and triumphantly sets his foot onto the slightly dusty plate where he had stood just moments ago to crush the ball, which launched him into legend. After walking away from the plate, McGwire was met by his teammate, and the next scheduled hitter, center fielder Ray Lankford. With Ray, he exchanges forearm shivers, followed the patented McGwire fist to the stomach. The blow is light enough to cause no serious damage, however, the force behind this fist seems to have extra emotion behind it. The emotion In the stadium at this point is unreal. So thick, you almost have to brush it away from your face.

Within seconds, Mark is mobbed by several of his teammates to congratulate him. After the congratulations from his team, Mark turns his attention to his 10-year.old son, the Cardinal batboy, Matt McGwire. He lifts Matt's entire 110-pound frame up high into the air and says a few words to him. He sets him down and continues to receive more congratulations from teammates. Then he lifts Matt into the air again and says a few more words to him and gives him a loving fatherly kiss.

Big Mac turns his attention to one of his opponents, Chicago's right fielder, Sammy Sosa, who with 58 home runs at the time, was his closest competitor. He embraces Sammy and lifts all 200 pounds of Sosa into the air with ease and adulation to the deafening roar of the crowd. After he sets him down, Mark and Sammy exchange forearm shivers and fists. Then, in an act of true friendship, McGwire does Sosa's post homerun celebration. He kisses his index and middle finger, and then taps his heart, and then repeats it again. Sammy then embraces Mark and congratulates him once more.

He blows a few kisses to the crowd, pumps his fists, then he turns his attention to the family of Roger Maris, the former Yankee great who hit 61 in '61. He runs over to the front row box seats and leaps right in. He embraces all six of Roger Maris' children.

In the words of Joe Buck: "Folks, it couldn't happen to a better man."

*(Barnhart is a freelance writer from Midland, Michigan.)*

# Why this bleacher bum hates Ernie Banks

**by Mark W. Schraf**

How utterly simple for you
to constantly say let's play two.
While most of us fans have to work,
you stand there at first with a smirk
on your face. And why not? After all,
the Wrigley's pay you to play ball.
I wonder how long you would last
if somehow you got working-classed
and had to haul trash everyday
to smell bad for almost no pay.
Or sit at a desk and count beans
or stack and load tons of sardines.
You've got no idea how hard,
embittered, worn-out, battle-scarred
a life in the school of hard knocks

will make you. Instead all you jocks
get paid fifty times what we do.
It's all one more turn of the screw.
So I'll drink beer and boo when I want
if you so much as act nonchalant.
I paid my two bucks to get in,
I've earned it! I'll curse you, has-been!
Besides, my soul's Beelzebub's
already - I'm cursed for the Cubs!
I could've found pleasure in life
A respite from all of my strife.
My baseball team could've been winners:
I must be the worst of all sinners.
But the Cubs sure as hell ain't the Yanks.
No wonder I hate Ernie Banks!

*(Schaf is a member of the Society For American Baseball Research and fiction editor for Spitball Magazine.)*

# Play ball, Bill!

**by Charles T. Grilley**

'Twas at a baseball game one day,
Where I was passing an hour away,
I chanced to hear some wisdom rare,
The last thing I looked for there.

'Twas from the catcher, a wise old fox,
Who was coaching a youngster in the box
Who badly needed a kindly word
And these are the ones I overheard:

Get 'em over the plat, Bill, play ball for fair!
Keep your feet on the ground, boy! Don't go up in the air!
Many a race has been landed, when it looked in doubt,
No game is lost, Bill, till the last man's out.

Could Solomon wise, in world or deed,

Give better advice to a friend in need?
And oftentimes in life's great game,
When trouble and worry around me came,
I thought of the catcher and once heard more
The voice of cheer and the helpful word,
And they served a mission and smoothed my way,
As they helped his pal in the box that day.

Get 'em over the plat, Bill, play ball for fair!
Keep your feet on the ground, boy! Don't go up in the air!
Many a race has been landed, when it looked in doubt,
No game is lost, Bill, till the last man's out.

*(Reprinted from Werner's Readings and Recitations, 1916.)*

# When does the game start

A Detroit fan tells a story of a girl whom he took to see a game in that city.

"She told me she knew all about the game, and when the players got on the field before the game to warm up, she asked me what they were doing. I told her they were practicing.

"The game started and she never uttered a world until about the seventh inning, when she leaned over to me and said: 'Say, Grover, when are they going to start the game?'"

*(Reprinted from Around the World with the Baseball Bugs, 1910.)*

# A blessing in disguise

**by W.C. Madden**

Dave Dravecky's baseball career was going along like smooth highway with just a few bumps. The left-handed pitcher was a winner on the mound the first five seasons of his career. He had also appeared in a World Series and two League Championship Series.

The lefty was hoping to get 20 wins in 1988, but arm problems derailed that plan. Doctors found a tumor in his arm and had to remove half of his deltoid muscle. They told him that he'd never pitch again. He had other ideas.

He worked his way back to the majors. On August 10, 1989 in his second start of the season, he was pitching in the sixth inning when his arm suddenly broke. The unforgettable action was caught on television. The strain had been too much for his arm to take. It had to be amputated.

Dravecky went through some depressing times before he found God, who helped him get over his tragedy.

He now looks at the cancer as a blessing. He took the occasion to write about a book about it for other people to learn from his experience.

*(Editor's Note: The book, "Do Not Lose Heart: Meditations of Encouragement and Comfort," is available at amazon.com.)*

# The difference

**by William F. Kirk**

"It's just this way," said Danny O'Shay,
As he whittled a stick and the hours away,
"A player can booze for a year or two,
The same as me or the same as you.
You meet a ball-gamer now and then
Who can guzzle more than the most of men.
But sooner or later he has to go
The way I was chased from the big league show.

"The difference, kid," said Danny O'Shay,
"Between the hard and the easy way,
As far as ball players goes, at least,
Is a difference big as the West and East.
I played ten years before I was spurned,
And this is the lesson your uncle learned:
The boozer THINKS he is splitting the wood,
The man that is sober KNOWS he's good.

"You see," continued Danny O'Shay,
"A dog and a man must have his day.
I played like a demon for seven years,
'Till I switched to whiskey and quit my beers,
I laughed at the friends that steered me right,
But here's the difference, black and white:
The boozer THINKS he is splitting the wood,
The man that is sober KNOWS he's good.

*(Reprinted from Right Off the Bat.)*

# It ain't the same

**by Wesley Swims**

Opening Day for baseball fans is one of the most exciting days of the year. On one particular opening day, Joey and his father skipped school and work, respectively, to watch the Cardinals play the Mets on television. Joey was in the sixth grade, so it wasn't too hard to play hooky. His father, on the other hand, had a tougher go at it but managed to get by with it.

At one point, as they watched, Joey noticed that the stadium was packed with people who looked like they were having a lot of fun. Something bothered him though and he turned to his father with a quizzical look.

"Daddy, why are there so many people there?" Joey asked.

"What are you talking about? They're watching the game just like us," he replied.

"Why don't they just stay home and watch it like us?"

"Because it isn't the same."

Joey looked at his father with confusion. "It ain't?"

"Nope. By the way, it isn't, not ain't." The two watched the rest of the game in silence.

That night as Joey lay in bed, he wondered what his father had meant by it not being the same. He often didn't understand. He thought about this for a while and eventually fell asleep dreaming of large crowds and grand slams.

Two months later, Joey was celebrating his eleventh birthday. He opened gifts from relatives and friends, blew out candles, and took a thousand pictures. After the party, when everyone had left, his father sat him on his lap. "Joey there is one more gift you need to open."

"Where?" Joey gasped.

His father reached in his shirt pocket and pulled out a small envelope. "Here."

Joey snatched the envelope from his hand and tore it open. Inside were colorful pieces of paper.

"They're tickets, Joey. Me and you are going to see the Cardinals play."

Joey had never been so excited in his short life. "Wow! We are actually goin'?"

"Yep, this weekend."

During the week Joey slept, ate, and drank baseball. He could hardly wait to see the big ball park and all those people.

The weekend finally arrived, which seemed like decades to Joey. He and his father drove the four-hour trip to St. Louis to watch the Cardinals play the Pirates. When they arrived, they had to drive downtown where Busch Stadium was located. The trip to the park was eventful itself.

Joey was in awe of everything from the Mississippi River to Arch. Joey noticed huge jets in the sky when his father tapped him on the shoulder.

"There's the stadium."

Joey turned to look and his eyes widened in excitement. His father pulled the car into a parking garage that was located just across the street. The two jumped out and made their way toward the stadium.

They reached an opening where a man asked Joey for his ticket. Joey had slept with that ticket and had taken it everywhere he went. He reluctantly gave the man his ticket and watched as the man ripped the edge off. Joey stared in horror but felt a little better when the man gave him the bigger half back.

Inside, a woman in a red coat helped the two find their seats. As soon as Joey sat down his senses became alive. The place was crowded with people, most of them wearing red, like he saw on television. He saw the players on the field and some other guys wetting the infield with a hose that hooked up behind the mound. Joey had never seen grass so green in his life! He heard the snap of baseballs hitting gloves as the players warmed up. He felt a warm breeze in his face. He could smell popcorn, nachos, and hot dogs which made him very hungry. He could also smell that yellow stuff that his father sometimes drank with friends on Fridays. Joey was beginning to understand what his dad had meant.

After the game on the way home, Joey slept off the four hot dogs he had eaten while clutching a pennant his father had bought him. Joey woke up halfway through the trip home and stared at his dad.

"Dad, you were right."

His father looked at him. "About what son?"

"It ain't the same."

Joey laid his head back down and slept the rest of the way home, dreaming of large crowds and home runs.

*(Swims is a freelance writer from Cape Girardeau, Missouri.)*

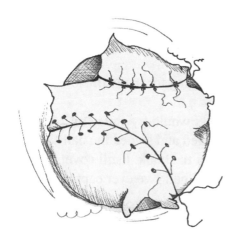

# The foul ball

**by W.C. Madden**

For most fans, the most treasured item at any professional baseball gale is the 9-inch white sphere, because it is so hard to obtain. Kids come armed with baseball gloves to catch it and grown-ups carry nets to snag it.

I had been going to baseball games ever since I was in Little League and had never once got my hands on one of those elusive balls.

Then it finally happened. I was 45 years old at the time and working on my first book about Hoosiers who had played the game. I was attending a game at Bush Stadium in Indianapolis with my wife on Aug. 31, 1993. I had a press pass, but I preferred to sit in the stands. We chose seats in right field in a sparsely occupied section to watch the Indianapolis Indians. Nobody sat in the row behind us, which was up against a wall.

I was intently watching the game when Ron

Coomer fouled off a pitch. The ball sailed over the corner of the roof and landed in the row behind us. I turned and grabbed it up.

Several children came begging for the ball. No way. I wasn't going to give it up.

After the game, I decided I would try and get it autographed by Coomer. He obliged and signed the ball for me. I used the ball on the cover of the book. I still covet that ball today as it is the only foul ball I've ever captured.

# Last game

**by Andrea Blaha**

Uniforms donned with casual familiarity
Gloves softened and molded just right
Spitting, although second nature, perfected to an art
Left fielder, hands on hips, exhorting the pitcher to "make
him hit"
Caps dusty and dirty with sweat lines and memories of
close calls
Hearing "I hate that pitch" once more from the one kid on
the team
who didn't make much progress and who, yet again, took a
called third strike
Water bottles passed around, shared easily
"Speedy," "Slugger," "Rocket"–nicknames earned not
easily given
Hooting, hollering, slaps on the back–release of
little-kid exuberance in adolescent bodies
A simultaneous sign of relief and a flicker of self-chastise

ment for doubting,
from the coaches as the center-fielder makes the catch to
the end the game
And from the parents a swell of pride at the victory
and hope that family life will now get back to normal
Knowing full well that normal involves practices and
games
for the next sport in season

*(Blaha is a freelance writer from Bowling Green, Ohio.)*

# Recollections on Forbes Field

**by Craig E. Galik**

My favorite recollection of Forbes Field was getting there early on a Sunday morning after leaving our home at about ten o'clock in the morning with a lunch sack full of sandwiches for Skip, Denny and me. We didn't care what time we got home, the later the better.

It was nice to think we spent the whole day at the ball park for only a dollar each and we saw two baseball games. We sometimes spent a quarter for a large Coke.

My biggest disappointment at Forbes Field was sitting in right field like all fans of Roberto Clemente did and yelling, "Arriba! Arriba!" (That was Clemente's nickname.) But the great Clemente would never acknowledge our screams. He just ignored us. He was one of the best ball players I ever saw, but his personality left a lot to be desired.

When the Pirates would start a rally during a ball game, the fans would kick the backs of the seats and the noise would sound like a train approaching. I would look for the train but there was none. Forbes Field was called the "House of Thrills" but for me it was a place of dreams where I hoped that some day I would be able to show off my skills for the crowd.

We weren't regular visitors to Forbes Field. We couldn't afford to be, but whenever we had the opportunity to go to a game, we went. Some of the best games we went to were on "Knothole" days, when Little Leaguers were admitted free on Saturday afternoon. We usually went with our uniforms on to gain the free entry. We sat in the right field bleachers and watched for batted balls that might hit the beams and bounce back and hit us. At one Saturday game, Wes Covington hit a home run that said deep to right, hit a bean and bounced back right into my seat. I didn't see the ball, but I felt a pain in the back of my neck when it hit me.

After those "Knotholer" days, the next time I went and saw the Pirates was in Three Rivers Stadium in 1979 for the World Series. The players and the stadium were never the same again.

*(Reprinted with permission from Galik's book, "Rounding Third and Heading Home.")*

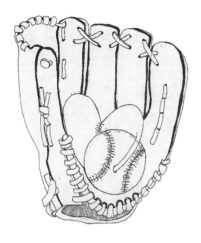

# My baseball glove

**by David Dixon Margolis**

My old Mizuno died last week
Oh, I hate to put it that way
Had to replace it
Tried to relace it
Worked for a while, too
But then other laces started to go
And it was beyond my skills

Too expensive for a pro to work on, I figured
Kind of silly and indulgent
And I'd rather, I guess, it sat in my Mets bag
All broken and tattered
Than to be dissected by some stranger

Eighteen years I'd had that glove
Right after I got married
Had a Wilson before that

But it was in the trunk when my car was stolen
Found the car
On Florence and Normandy
Where the riot started
Stripped and ravaged and left for dead
But I got it running again
Sort of

But the Wilson was gone
Next day, I imagine, the thief snared a liner deep in the hole
Nice piece of leather, homie, the third baseman called over
Through gold-plated teeth
And the price was right too, bro
High fives and knuckle bumps all around the infield

She didn't know anything about gloves
My wife
My husband plays mostly softball
She told that man at Hollywood Star Sporting Goods
He likes to play third base
He has big hands
Long fingers

I hope I didn't spend too much, she said
Presenting me with the Mizuno
And for once she hadn't

A great glove
Perfect
It fit my hand like the cliche'
Sucked up short hops like nothing
A cozy place for line drives to disappear

Over time it got so comfortable
And loose fitting

I could extend and retract it
with the slightest flexing of my fingertips
Like a telescope

It got a lot more use when the boy came along
Got interested in baseball
Dedicated
Obsessed
Work on your throws, I'd shout to him
Throwing grounders
I can catch them but your teammates won't

Once he threw a wild pitch
My arm shot out
The glove slipped off and flew away
About 20 feet
When I picked it up
The ball was inside
I mean *inside*
Where your hand goes

Never do that again if I tried
Not in a million years

Bought a new Wilson last week
He talked me into the expensive one
You'll have it forever, Dad, you'll use it all the time

He was right
Probably the last glove I'll ever own, too
He agreed too quickly

Dark and thick and padded
Snug
But not so good at scooping short hops

What are you doing
He asked all panicky
When I took off my wedding ring to make more room
Where you gonna put it

On my key ring
In my bag
It'll be safe

You can't lose that, Dad,
All scared and serious
You can never lose that

*(Margolis is a member of the Society for American Base-
ball Research.)*

# Tragedy in the Negro Leagues

**by W.C. Madden**

Back in 1942, many tragedies were occurring overseas with the war going on, but the Negro Leagues had their own to contend with.

A group of players and the owner of the Cincinnati Buckeyes were driving back to Cincinnati from a series with the New York Black Yankees when they had a flat tire in the wee hours of September 7. After repairing the tire around 3 a.m., Ulysses "Buster" Brown reentered the highway just west of Geneva, Ohio, but not fast enough for a truck barrelling down the road. The truck driver couldn't stop in time and crashed into the back of the car.

Brown and Raymond "Smoky" Owens were killed instantly. Eugene Bremer and Herman Watts were hospitalized, while Alonzo Boone and owner Wilbur Hayes escaped with minimal injuries.

Brown had played six seasons in the Negro Leagues, while Owens was a four-year veteran.

# Gridiron greats not so great at baseball

**by Bob Kitchel**

Three of the greatest legends in professional and college football history had unique–even bizarre–brief careers in the Major Leagues.

They were Jim Thorpe, George Halas and Ernie Nevers, all members of the Pro Football Hall of Fame in Canton, Ohio.

Both Thorpe and Nevers were not over-the-hill when they quit baseball. Thorpe was 33 when he retired from the old Boston Braves after the 1919 season. Nevers was a mere 25 when he opted to exit the old St. Louis Browns after 1928.

The shocking thing about them is that they had a "career year" in their final year in the bigs. They were both at their best. Of course, their final numbers were nowhere near a Joe DiMaggio, a George Brett or a Christy

Mathewson.

While the records of Thorpe and Nevers are well-documented, the Major League experience of Halas is usually reduced to a trivia question: Who preceded Babe Ruth as the Yankee right fielder? Hey, that's a great question, except it is not only false, but ludicrous.

Papa Bear, in fact, was a fine baseball player and offensive end for the Fighting Illini. Supposedly, baseball was his favorite sport and he did well in the minors. His major league service, however, was limited to a slice of 1919, when he had all of 22 at bats, got two hits and retired with a batting average of .091. This aggressive young man had other endeavors to pursue.

The guy The Babe effectively replaced in the Yankees outfield was a solid player named Ping Bodie, who had 1,009 more hits than Halas.

Back to Thorpe and Nevers.

Jim Thorpe is arguably one of the greatest athletes of all time. He broke in with McGraw's Giants in 1913 at age 27, one year removed from his Olympic heroics at Stockholm. He hit an ugly .143 in nine games. He upped that to .194 in 30 games the next year.

Thorpe finally became a semi-regular with the Reds and Giants in 1917, had 308 at bats and hit .237. He also had 12 stolen bases that year, the high water mark in pilfers from the speed demon. He hit .248 in 113 at bats for the Giants in 1919.

Then in 1919, he turned it around. Thorpe put it together and hit .327 in 159 at bats with 26 RBI. After that sold season, mostly with the hapless Braves in Boston, he bid adieu to the majors.

His surprising farewell at age 33 was prompted by a meeting that winter in a pace called Canton with people called Halas and Lambeau. And the dye for a new professional sport was case. Thorpe was not only pro football's first president but also its star gate attraction.

The Major League career of Ernie Nevers was the first of the California surfer-types, even though a Minnesota native. He played three years for the St. Louis Browns, beginning in 1926. His overall record was 6-12 on the mound with a 4.64 ERA. He gave up 196 hits in 178 1/3 innings during the three years and allowed 61 walks compared to 39 Ks. But he did complete six of twelve starts.

Nevers was awesome in football at Stanford and for the old Chicago Cardinals in the pro league that Halas and Thorpe organized. In fact, Nevers scored a record 40 points against the hated Chicago Bears on Thanksgiving Day in 1929. He scored six TDs and kicked four-of-six extra points.

Never, suffering a "sore arm," called it quits from baseball after 1928, when he was 1-0 with a nice 3.00 ERA, his best year, although abbreviated.

As Mel Allen would say, "How about that."

*(Kitchel is a former reporter in Chicago.)*

# Base instincts

**by Steven Bartel**

There's this game we call "Base"
It's played with a ball
And it's all the "hot spit" in camp.
There's a "hurler" who throws at a man with a bat
(who must whack it or bear its stamp.)

And if he fends off this assault with dispatch
he can give that ball "leagues to roam"
and sprint round the great "diamond" of bases...
(Be it ever so humble, there's no base like home.)

–Pvt. Hell
1st Minnesota Volunteer Infantry
Army of the Potomac

*(Bartel is a freelance writer from Los Angeles.)*

# Wrong place at the wrong time

**by W.C. Madden**

Many good players sometimes fail to get much of a chance at the majors because they were in the wrong place at the wrong time. That's how you could describe the career of Scottie Earl.

Scottie attended at high school in the boondocks of Indiana, which was the first wrong place. Scouts didn't see him, so he wasn't drafted after graduating from high school.

Then he attended Glen Oaks Junior College where scouts again didn't see him, so he went to a Cincinnati Reds tryout. Unable to impress the scouts, he attended Eastern Kentucky where he finally got the exposure he needed.

Then the Detroit Tigers drafted him in 1981. "Six teams called me the day before the draft," he explained. "I was kind of disappointed I was drafted in the fourteenth round."

After a solid season at Triple-A Evansville, Scottie was beamed to the majors in September with the Tigers way ahead in the pennant race. The day after Earl was put in the lineup for the first time, the team clinched the pennant. The rest of the month he appeared in 14 games and hit .114. The Tigers went to the World Series without him. So he went off to play winter ball.

The next spring, he was hoping to get another shot at the majors, but the Tigers brought up Chris Pittaro from Double-A and sent him to Triple-A. "It was one of the biggest disappointiments of my career. I was expected to make the team," he said.

After a solid season in Triple-A, he didn't get the call in September either. After spring training the next year, he was again assigned to Nashville. The Tigers had Lou Whitaker at second base. "I was an insurance policy," he explained.

The following season he broke his left tibia, which put him out for two months. Then he became a free agent and signed with the Cincinnati Reds. He had a great spring, but the Reds decided to use Jeff Treadway at second instead of him and he was sent to Triple-A. But jus a couple of days before the season began, the Reds called for him back. He played two exhibition games. On Opening Day, the traveling team secretary called him to give him bad news. He wasn't needed after all and was sent to Triple-A.

After the 1989 season ended, he was released. Several teams called him about playing, but none would assure him he would play. "I wanted to play in the big leagues or do something else," he commented.

Scottie decided on the something else and settled down in Indianapolis with a family and a regular job.

# The curved bat

As if the game itself was not freakish enough, Pat Dougherty went to bat in the ninth inning with a freak stick which had a concave curve near its end, designed to add to the uncertainties of the game by enabling batsmen to put a curve on the ball when they hit it, making it more difficult to field. That is the claim of its inventor (Emile Kinst), and it seem to deliver the goods. Dougherty hit a fly toward center, which Cobb went after, but the ball sailed away from him toward Crawford and and resulted in a double for Pat. Sullivan debated for some time whether to use the freak or his own bat, then chose the former. He popped a fly to Lindsay which came down with a more pronounced curve than pop flies usually have.

*(Reprinted from the Chicago Tribune, 1910.)*

# Miracle makes Morris a major leaguer

**By Joe Henderson**

*(The following story was published on Sept. 26, 1999 in the Tampa Tribune and is reprinted with permission.)*

It was just another Saturday afternoon in a tumbleweed town two stops from nowhere on the central Texas prairie. It was really too hot for this sort of thing. The mid-June sun sent 104 degrees to bleed the patience and enthusiasm from Doug Gassaway as he waited for 70 wanna-bes to finish wasting his time at a tryout camp for the Tampa Bay Devil Rays.

"Not a one of 'em could play a lick," he said.

Gassaway, a regional scout and graying baseball lifer who has sent more than 90 players to the major leagues, had spent about two hours in that oven when he looked at the last guy in line. Jimmy Morris. He was carrying 25 pounds more than he should around the middle. He

had a baby in his arms, one holding on to his legs, and he
was pushing a third in a stroller.

Morris was 35 years old and looked it. His hairline
was receding, there were flecks of gray around the temples.
He wore softball pants. Gassaway rolled his eyes.

"I looked at him and said, 'C'mon Jimmy, I'm hot
and I'm tired. Let's get this over with so I can go home,'"
Gassaway said.

What happened next cannot happen anywhere
except the movie of the week. In those moments that
followed, Jimmy Morris became The Natural, or Kevin
Costner in a cornfield, or any other bit of Hollywood sap
you can swallow–except this was very, very real.

Ask Royce Clayton of the Texas Rangers, an accomplished big-league hitter who struck out against Morris
on Sept. 18 on four very, very hard pitches in a game at The
Ballpark in Arlington.

Or ask Jim Edmonds, Mo Vaughn and Tim Salmon
of the Anaheim Angels–combined salary this season, $16.1
million. Morris set them down in order two nights later.

Yes, indeed, it could be a movie, but it isn't. He has
come from the most obscure of outposts and beat the most
daunting of odds to win a spot in the Rays' bullpen. He is
the oldest rookie to join a big-league team since the Minnesota Twins called up Minnie Mendoza in 1970.

"We've heard from every major network and several major studios about making this a movie," Rays Vice
President of Public Relations Rick Vaughn said. "We've
heard from Sports Illustrated, ESPN, Dateline NBC, CBS
This Morning ... you name it. We had a guy call and want
to do the screenplay. I have been in baseball 17 years and
have never seen anything like it."

It isn't like Morris doesn't have the background to

succeed. He was a No. 1 draft pick of the Milwaukee Brewers–OK, it was in 1983. His pro career didn't amount to much; arm problems kept him from advancing beyond Class A ball. He hung 'em up in 1989 after having surgery to remove a bone spur in his left arm. He settled into the role of husband, father, high school teacher and baseball coach. He drove 70 miles one-way each day to Reagan County High School in Big Lake, Texas–population 3,672–where he taught chemistry, integrated physics and biology.

He also coached the baseball team and pitched batting practice every day during the season. He figures he built up arm strength that way. In fact, the kids used to complain he threw too hard, but Morris figured they were just trying to get out of extra work. Then, last spring, he was in the middle of a typical coach speech–work hard, believe in yourself, follow your dreams, yada yada yada– when a couple of kids spoke up.

"What about your dreams, coach?"

"They thought I still wanted to be in the major leagues," he said.

So Morris made them a deal. If they won the district title, he would try out for a big-league club.

They won.

To pay his debt, he loaded his three kids in a dusty Olds Cutlass and drove to the campus of Howard Payne University in Brownwood; his wife, Lorrie, was giving entrance exams to would-be students at Angelo State University in San Angelo.

"I figured all I was doing was fulfilling my promise to my high school kids," he said. "After that, I could go and get another job in teaching and get back on with my life."

The guys at the camp all looked so young; compared to him, they were young. He almost didn't get out of the car. But then he started to pitch. His first warm-up throw came in at 94 miles an hour. "I looked at the guy next to me and said, 'My [radar] gun is broken, let me see yours,'" Gassaway said. "The guy told me, no, my gun wasn't broken."

Next pitch: 96 mph.

"I turn to the guy and said, 'There has to be some electrical interference here,'" Gassaway said. "He said, 'No, there wasn't.'"

Next pitch: 95. Then 12 straight throws at 98 mph.

When Lorrie got home from work, there were several messages on the recorder, each one the same: Call Doug Gassaway. He had checked with Rays' officials and they wanted Morris to come back in two days to throw again.

Jimmy was floating. Lorrie was supportive but understandably skeptical.

She understood all about Morris" baseball dream. He had turned down football scholarships to Penn State and Notre Dame–he was a punter–because those schools wouldn't let him play baseball. He went to Angelo State on an academic scholarship.

They had met on a blind date while he was near the end of his first try at professional baseball. She was with him when that dream ended.

"I never wanted to stand in the way of any dreams. I never wanted him to say, "I might have been able to do it if Lorrie hadn't stayed in the way."

But I didn't want him to get hurt, either," she said.

"I would say, 'Jimmy, is this what you really ought to be doing at this point in your life? Take your ability, but teach your guys and give them the opportunities you didn't get.'"

Of course, at that point she could not have known the opportunity her husband was about to get. Who could have?

It was raining when Morris showed up for his second throwing session, of course. Raining hard. They waited two hours but the rain wouldn't stop. Morris shrugged finally and went to a bullpen mound; the regular pitcher's mound was too slippery. Mike Kennemer, baseball coach at Howard Payne, volunteered to be the catcher.

"He used to come out and work out with the university team here, but he never threw that hard, high '80s, top," Kennemer said. "Well, sir, on about the fourth or fifth pitch, he busts the laces on my mitt. I had to catch everything else down in the palm. My thumb was all black and blue the nextday and my hand was swollen."

Gassaway had seen enough. He offered Morris a minor-league contract.

That's where things got serious for Lorrie. After all, she would have to care for their three children and hold down her full-time job while Jim pursued his dream. She and Jimmy are devout Southern Baptists, so she did the only thing she knew how to for something like this.

She prayed.

"When they called, it's like, "OK, when are you going to go, how long are you going to be gone, how much money will you be making?" You know, real-life stuff. He wasn't thinking about that," she said.

"I kept thinking, "OK, Lord, you know what's going on here. This wasn't in our plans." But you know how I know it's right? The day Jimmy flew out, we got a call from a high school in Fort Worth about a job he had applied for. The athletic director called up to offer him the position. If he had called before, who knows?"

The Rays put him through some intensive physical work to lose his midlife spare tire, then put him on the roster with the Double-A minor-league team in Orlando.

After just three games, he was promoted to Triple-A in Durham, N.C.

If that was as far as it went, the story would still be amazing.

But it wasn't.

Late last week, Durham was eliminated from the International League playoffs. Morris was ready to head back to Texas. He and teammate Bobby Munoz had loaded a truck with their belongings for the drive when Durham manager Bill Evers called Morris to his office.

Evers was smiling.

"He told me I was going to the major leagues," Morris said.

Lorrie rustled up the kids for the four-hour drive to Arlington, Texas, a week ago Saturday for Jimmy's big-league debut. It was the first time the family had been together since he left June 23.

"I already got my tears out when I saw him in the bullpen," she said. "He looked so happy in his uniform and on the field, that smile on his face."

He entered the game with two out in the eighth inning against Clayton.

"I felt like my heart was going to jump out of my chest," he said. Four pitches–95, 95, 96, 95. Clayton trudged back to the dugout, a strikeout victim. Rays catcher John Flaherty stuck the ball in Morris" hand when he arrived back at the bench.

Welcome to the big leagues.

Back in their hotel room, Jimmy ordered a pizza for everyone and they tried to soak it all in. It has been a dizzying ride.

He is being paid a prorated portion of the annual big-league minimum salary of $200,000, meaning he'll make around $20,000 for this short ride until the end of the season Oct. 3. However, the Rays want him to attend the

Arizona Fall League next month and probably will invite him to spring training in 2000 with a chance to make the club for a full season. It still doesn't make much sense. Stories like this just don't happen, and who knows how long it will last? Doesn't matter. If it ends tomorrow, the ride has been a blast.

"When he first left, I cried and cried and cried," Lorrie said. "This was just beyond anything I could have ever dreamed of. It was stepping out in faith. It was totally crazy, but I figured there had to be a reason for this.

"So, after a while, it was like, "OK, this is where Jimmy is supposed to be." We both believe that. He is where he's supposed to be. So we know whatever happens, it's going to work out and it will all be for the best.

It's in God's hands.

*(Editor's Note: Morris played for Tampa Bay for a short time in 2000 and is now writing his own book on his miracle.)*

# Answers to Team Trivia Quiz

1. Dodgers
2. Reds
3. Expos
4. Indians
5. Padres
6. Giants
7. Cardinals
8. Braves
9. Phillies
10. White Sox
11. Rockies
12. Rangers
13. Mariners
14. Brewers
15. Royals
16. Yankees
17. Red Sox
18. Angels
19. Pirates
20. Diamondbacks
21. Twins
22. Astros
23. Mets
24. Orioles
25. Tigers
26. Athletics
27. Devil Rays
28. Marlins
29. Cubs
30. Blue Jays